D1076368

...d McConville was born in 1956 and spent her childhood in Malaysia, Sri Lanka, Canada, England and Ireland. She began her writing career as a freelance journalist in Dublin, and then moved to London to work for *Business Traveller* magazine. In 1981 she was runner-up in the Catherine Pakenham Award for young women journalists for her article on prostitution in Bangkok. After a spell at *Woman* magazine, she returned to freelance work, contributing to the *Independent*, the *Daily Telegraph*, *The Times*, the *Evening Standard*, the *Daily Mail*, the *Guardian*, *CHIC* magazine, *Choice*, *SHE* and *Marie Claire*. She is the author of *Sisters*, *Mad To Be A Mother*, *The Parent's Green Guide* and *Mixed Messages: Our Breasts in our Lives*. She moved to Somerset in 1985 where she was a founder of *Justwomen* magazine and editor of the *Hinkley Inquirer* during the nuclear power Inquiry. She lives with her partner John Shearlaw and their children Maeve and Arthur.

Her involvement in various groups in the women's movement prompted her to look at her own and other women's drinking in a new light: Why do women drink? What are the particular patterns and problems of our drinking? And why has information about alcohol's especially damaging effects on women been so scarce and inaccessible? In exploring these questions she came to believe that women's drinking – now rapidly on the increase – can only be understood in the context of our position in society.

By the same author

Sisters
Mad To Be A Mother
The Parent's Green Guide
Mixed Messages: Our Breasts In Our Lives

BRIGID McCONVILLE

Women Under the Influence

Alcohol and Its Impact

Pandora
An Imprint of HarperCollinsPublishers

Pandora
An Imprint of HarperCollins*Publishers*
77–85 Fulham Palace Road,
Hammersmith, London W6 8JB

First published by Virago Press Ltd 1983
Published by Grafton Books 1991
Published by Pandora 1995
1   3   5   7   9   10   8   6   4   2

© Brigid McConville

Brigid McConville asserts the moral right
to be identified as the author of this work

A catalogue record for this book is available
from the British Library

ISBN 0 04 440919 2

Printed in Great Britain by HarperCollinsManufacturing Glasgow

CONTENTS

ACKNOWLEDGEMENTS

Thanks to the women of DAWN, especially Shirley Otto, Clare Wilson, Fiona Richmond, Chris Chambers and Elspeth Kyle, who have been an invaluable source of ideas and support. Thanks also to my original editor at Virago, Ruthie Petrie, who not only helped the book into shape but tried and tested its methods on her own drinking habits.

My friends and all my family have given me great encouragement, especially my sister Fran McConville, and Liz Mellon, Jane Salvage, Mark Cooper, Lou Scott, Hugh Cooper and John Shearlaw.

I am very grateful also to May Holland and Ronald Forbes who provided me with a great deal of information and encouragement, to Dr Roger Williams of King's College Hospital Liver Unit who kindly had Part Two of my manuscript checked, and to Mic Cheetham, who got the whole thing off the ground in the first place.

Roy Johnson, the ever-helpful librarian at Alcohol Concern, has been the most thorough and prompt source of information, together with Rachel Carter of Alcohol Concern.

Thanks also to Ann McIntyre of the Women's Alcohol Centre and Geraldine Nolan of DAWN for their suggestions and for their continuing commitment to women, as well as Sarah Berger of DRINKLINE.

The diagrams included here have been adapted from their originals. For permission to adapt and use, I would like to thank the Health Education Council for diagrams 2, p. 103, 3, p. 108, and 4, p. 109; Accept Services UK for diagram 5 on p. 115; and M. M. Glatt, MD, DPM, for diagram 6 on p. 190.

I especially want to thank all those women who gave me their time and courageously talked about their often painful experiences with alcohol. I am indebted to the women workers at AA, to the women of Women's Fightback, the Tulse Hill CR group, the Oxford House women's group and my other women friends without whom this book could not have been written.

OUT OF HER GRAVITY

She has thrust herself off
The shelf of the earth
Gone searching
For the white side of night.
Flight is the glass
Between her hands
Lifting her
Out of her gravity.

She climbs on the dark's back
Trusts it
Like a dolphin
To take her twisting
Along the rim
Of the world.
With every drink
She swallows a shoal of stars.

The glass is empty.
Light shatters her body
Exploding in the sea.
She hits the surface
And her mouth yawns wide,

A fish gulping air.
Nothing matters
But the wind brushing her tongue.

Liz Mellon

INTRODUCTION

When I wrote the first edition of *Women Under the Influence* more than ten years ago, there were no other books for women about women's drinking and the whole issue was just emerging from under an enormous weight of stigma.

There is still no other book that looks at the implications of drinking for women in the context of our culture; nor has the stigma around women's drink problems lifted. Indeed, the moral panic about women's drinking persists as strongly as ever, with the media ever eager to focus on our drinking – despite the fact that men still drink more, and abuse alcohol more.

Yet the increase in drinking and drink problems (for both men and women) is a continuing phenomenon of our times. Women's drinking has changed as our position as women has changed, and in the 1990s we are major consumers of alcohol.

It has been a mixed blessing. On the one hand, we generally have more freedom to drink, more money to spend and more opportunities to enjoy drinking. But, on the other, more women are becoming ill and dying as a result of drink. This book is for *all* women drinkers, because while most of us still enjoy 'a good drink', we all have the potential to lose control of our drinking and be destroyed by it.

The publicity about increases in women's drinking is often expressed as concern about a new 'women's problem'. But we need to be wary of the focus of this concern. For example, the increase in women's drinking has been blamed on feminism, and women's alcoholism has been called 'the ransom of emancipation'. One implication of current media headlines about 'Career Girls' hitting the bottle (and it is true that professional, married women with families are turning more to alcohol) is that our career ambitions – as opposed to our dual role as homemakers – are driving us to drink.

Scare tactics like these have been used against women in times of social change: the suffragettes were warned that their reproductive organs would wither, and in recent decades working mothers have been blamed for juvenile delinquency and mental breakdown.[1] We need to be careful that our drinking 'problems' are put in the context of the social pressures that push us into drinking rather than in terms of a 'moral panic' about a woman's rightful place – traditionally *not* in the pub.

I became interested in writing about women's drinking when a colleague of mine told me the story of her young daughter's disability. Her child had been born with some of the symptoms of Down's syndrome, but a series of doctors were unable to agree on a diagnosis. Eventually, after years of consulting specialists, one of these suggested that her daughter might be suffering from Foetal Alcohol Syndrome, or FAS.

She had never heard of this at the time, and nor had I when she told me. I was appalled to realise that I, who during my twenties had been a heavy drinker, had no clear idea of the effects of alcohol on my body. I began to find out about FAS and realized that this was only the tip of the iceberg. I didn't know and neither did my women friends, that alcohol affects us differently and more damagingly than men in all sorts of ways. Finding out about this was a struggle: there were virtually no books or articles on the subject that were well informed without being highly technical, obscure or plain inaccessible. So I set out to write a book to provide that information for women.

When I started I had no axe to grind, no theory to propound, but only my own background and family history of intermittent drinking problems. In the text books I found the occasional chapter about women drinkers, written by the experts (usually male), but from women drinkers themselves there was silence. I decided to start by interviewing as many women as possible about their own drinking, and the book starts with four of these women speaking at length about their drinking. (I have changed their names for the sake of privacy in this chapter and in subsequent ones; some place names have been changed for the same reason.)

Very soon a pattern began to emerge: very different women were saying the same sorts of things about themselves and their drinking. Whether 'social' drinkers or 'problem' drinkers, they talked about their feelings of oppression, inadequacy, shyness, anxiety, depression and lack of confidence as women.

These women come from all over the UK, and range in age from about fifteen to sixty-five; they come from different social classes and ethnic backgrounds. I interviewed them individually and in groups, through established agencies, personal contacts and women's groups.

Most of the women I talked to are white. Few black women attend the established agencies as clients, and there are few black workers in the alcohol field (see chapter 4). It also seems that in black groups, social problems tend to be contained within the community and dealt with, if at all, by the family and by the church. But if white women drink from frustration and a sense of oppression – while feeling they must hide their 'shameful' habit – how much more must black women have reasons to do the same?

Our perceptions and patterns of drinking must be seen against a background of social attitudes and expectations. Chapter 3, which is about the stereotyped image of women drinkers as portrayed in popular literature, advertisements and the media, supplies a part of this background. These are the 'norms' against which we are measured, and if we are to make sense of our behaviour we must look critically at these social and 'moral' yardsticks. This look at the conventional ideas about women drinkers raises the question: Is there something 'wrong' with us – or with 'normality'?

The emphasis in the opening chapters is on the social factors which affect women's drinking, but the nature of our society is such that decisions by governments, advertisers and the alcohol industry have a powerful influence on our drinking habits. The last chapter of Part One looks at the statistics about drinking and the economic and political factors that shape 'normality' – and our drinking destinies.

Part Two looks at the physical effects of alcohol on our bodies. We are far more prone than men to alcohol's intoxicating and damaging effects, and we must have a series of educational campaigns to inform us of the facts – if we are to make vital choices about our own, and our children's, health.

Part Three is written for women like myself who have worried that they are drinking for reasons, and to a level, which they feel unhappy about. I have suggested ways of self-help, and professional help, for those who decide they want to cut down.

I hope that women drinkers who read this book will recognize some of their own experience, and that, at the end of it, they will be able to use alcohol more healthfully, and more happily.

Part One

WOMEN AND ALCOHOL

1

WOMEN SPEAKING

Jane

My neighbours used to say to me, 'Jane, *why* do you drink? You've got four lovely children, a good home, a good husband.' I used to blame my husband and all sorts of things, but I really didn't know why I drank. Once I started I just couldn't stop.

It was my youngest son, Malcolm, who was most affected by my drinking. He was withdrawn and didn't play with other kids. He went to a special school three days a week and he asked to be called Malcolm at one school, and Nigel, his second name, at the other.

I didn't believe it was anything to do with my drinking. I rationalized that it was his teacher's fault, or that he was like his father, a loner.

I was ashamed of myself, and full of guilt about the effect on my family and about not being a 'normal' mother. I always wanted to be a 'good' mother – one who baked and sewed and sang lullabies and kept a beautiful home. But none of those things came naturally to me.

When my babies were born I thought there was supposed to be a big wave of emotion. I didn't feel it. I thought there was something missing in me and that I was inadequate. No one told me that you just feel tired and want to sleep and forget the whole thing.

I also felt very inadequate beside my sister and sister-in-law. Men always turned and looked at my sister – she was very sexy. My sister-in-law is a nurse, very capable. She cooked and sewed – and she could shatter me with the lift of an eyebrow. Until about three years ago I couldn't relate to women at all, especially women with nursing experience.

I got all my ideas from women's magazines. No one told me it's okay sometimes to *hate* your kids and feel trapped by children.

I came to London from Scotland when I was eighteen and I had never had a drink. I lived with my sister and I was very unhappy. So when I first saw the man who was to be my husband, Ken, I said to myself – I will marry him. It was his looks. He was to be my knight in shining armour, come to save me.

I was very immature and influenced by what others said. I believed in happy-ever-after and thought I would be secure for the rest of my life.

I married at nineteen and had a child in my first year. I started taking amphetamines for depression. They made me feel good and beautiful, and I thought then that I could match up to my sister-in-law's standards. I remember sitting there sewing for hours.

At twenty-five I was sent to a mental hospital because of my addiction to amphetamines. When I came out I started to go to pubs to drink 'socially' with friends. Booze made me feel good, the same as the pills had, and beautiful.

But I drank more than my friends. I always wanted more, drank faster and I wanted to stay until the bell rang in the pub. I could never stop. It still amazes me how people drink half a bottle of wine and leave the rest. I didn't get drunk every night, just Saturday night and Sunday lunch at that stage. It was no problem in between at that time – only later.

But drinking crept up on me very slowly and subtly. I used to get half a bottle of Scotch at Sunday lunch and invite a friend in. If she had a drink with me it made it more acceptable. But I had guilt at the back of my mind that my friends, the 'good mothers', didn't drink.

When my eldest daughter was sixteen, the twins were eleven and Malcolm was four, I went out to work as a telephonist. I started drinking a lot with a younger crowd from work. I enjoyed it. I rewarded myself. I thought I should enjoy my life now after having had the children.

I used to stay out late. My husband took very little notice. If he did say anything I would be angry with him. I told him he was a moron and I needed more stimulating company. I thought I was some kind of frustrated genius . . .

He used to get up, go to work, come home and watch the telly and go to bed. He is an electrician and has been doing the same job for twenty-odd years. He is a normal man, stable and happy in his way of life – but I thought something was wrong with it.

I needed to drink more and more. I started buying bottles and drinking all weekend. I couldn't cope with my family and the puberty of my daughter. She assumed the role of mother in the house and I was jealous. I was always shouting and very angry. And all through this was the guilt: I wasn't happy when I was working, and I wasn't happy when I wasn't working.

This went on for about five years, drinking whenever I could Then one time I met an alcoholic down-and-out in a pub. I had the money, he had the time. So I went to his 'skipper' [derelict site] to drink with him.

I thought I had found Paradise – drinking cheap wine at eight o'clock on a Saturday morning. I had no responsibility. I didn't have to wash on weekends. There was I, a middle-aged woman from a comfortable home, drinking in a derelict house . . . I wanted drink more than I wanted home, children or husband.

I lost my job through alcohol too. I was ready for promotion but we all got drunk in the office and later I was sacked. I started staying out later, and drinking more on weekends. I blamed my husband, blamed my children. I wanted to be free of them.

I got another job and lost it, again, through drink. I went on drinking at home then – when I could. When I had no money I had to stop. I started to lose care for myself. I became aggressive and fearful when I stopped drinking. One weekend when I was angry with my husband I swallowed a lethal dose of paracetamol and then told him.

I used to buy a bottle with my fish and chips and drink from Thursday to Monday. My husband didn't know how to cope. He stayed out of the house, and buried himself in work, pretending it wasn't happening.

By now I had attempted suicide five times – when I was drunk and felt sorry for *me*. The last attempt ended in intensive care. I can't tell if I ever really wanted to die; I was always drunk when I did it. When I came *off* booze, in midweek, then I would have wanted to die.

After about three years of drinking at home I had no relation-ship with my family whatsoever. My daughter told me only last week that the children thought the lady who drank came out of a bottle; it wasn't their mum. But I didn't know this.

My children tried everything to stop me: anger, love, leaving me alone, shouting, asking why? When I said I didn't want to drink alone but I was forced to, my daughter even drank along with me. She drank as I did – but I didn't want to share my booze.

Then my eldest daughter left home, and the twins were teenagers and always staying out. Just little Malcolm was there and going to the pub for my booze. I made him come home from school to get my bottle at lunchtime. I stayed in my bedroom mostly. I was dirty. I didn't wash or cook.

I used to wander sometimes in the streets. At forty I went to the Embankment to try and be a hippy. I went to a disco that my daughter went to. I made obscene phone calls. I kept running away. My home life was just a mess. I was desperately lonely and afraid.

Then a lady I knew came to talk to me. She didn't condemn me or ask me why I was drinking. She just asked if I had a problem. It was a tremendous relief to be able to say yes. She spoke to me with love and understanding. She came with me to a phone box and I phoned AA [Alcoholics Anonymous]. That was six years ago.

Three beautiful women took me to a meeting in their car. I was afraid of them. I was seventeen stone and I had no decent clothes. I had to have three valium tablets and a martini to get me to my first meeting.

I was afraid of AA – I thought it was like a temperance society. But I took to it like a duck to water. I stopped drinking. I had no terrible withdrawal symptoms. I began to take an interest in myself and in my family. It happened. My family were thrilled. My daughter moved home again. She used to wash my hair before every meeting and call for a cab for me. Immediately the family situation got better.

It was a very slow process but I discovered I was a very *angry* woman. I was very angry at women. They petrified me. If a woman walked into the room I would always feel inferior and inadequate. Now the anger is gone.

All of my life was based on what society made me be. So many people told me to do things. Coming to *see* for myself what it really is about – that took away the anger.

Now I have an identity. I know what I like. I like being with people. I like country and western music, and I like reading. I'm not really an extrovert; I like my own company too. And I go to AA meetings two or three times a week. I've been sober now for six years.

At first I still felt guilt. I even still wanted to be a 'good mother'. I did lots of washing and cleaning – and found I was getting resentful when my daughter left the bath dirty!

But I came to realize that I was a good mother, became a sick mother and now I'm an okay mother. I'm pretty average. They love me and I love them. Yes, my identity is being a mother – not a wife or a career woman.

Two years ago my two sons were killed in accidents, little Malcolm six weeks after his elder brother. Without the fellowship of AA I would never have survived it.

But they both had four years of me sober before they died. Malcolm, who had been going to a special school, could by then read and write and swim and play football. My oldest was a head chef. I knew that in that time I had been a better mother to them than ever.

After a year in AA I realized that my marriage had died. We didn't want to sleep together after all those years. Now we have a good friendship. Now I am more understanding of Ken, the man. He is not in the role of protector or provider. It really is a good relationship. The children accept it. We still live together and he still works hard. He is reasonably happy. He accepts himself.

I am happy too. I have peace of mind. I believe in God. I don't know that I *love*: I like, I care, I understand. I do *care* passionately.

I don't give a damn who knows I'm an alcoholic. I couldn't say what alcoholism is. I just know I've got it, and I can do something about it. I was born with this disease and this personality, so I don't drink.

People who are not alcoholic sometimes drink for the same reasons I did – because they feel inadequate or tired. But they don't go *on* drinking. In the alcoholic, the feelings of guilt, fear and anger go *so* deep . . . My anger leaves me physically and mentally exhausted even now.

I think it's okay to get angry if I'm angry for a good reason. Now I try to expend it by writing it down. It is a good thing too to redirect this anger, this fierceness. That emotion is energy I am still angry, but not the destructive anger that turns inwards that lasts and lasts. I don't feel that consuming guilt.

So many images are put on us whether we are male or female. It leaves you feeling that you have failed to be the Sexy Woman or the Good Mum. I don't *have* to wash and clean and sleep with my husband to be a good mother and wife. I *was* Ken's wife. I'm released from that image now.

I'm fat. People keep saying – you should slim. But I'm comfortable as I am. I'm quite happy being fourteen and a half stone. I like the image of being motherly. A fellow at our meeting said once, 'Jane, you know, you're dead sexy.' It made me want to say – ugh – go away, leave me alone.

So many women don't have a feeling of self-worth. There is so much pressure on us to be thin, to be glamorous, to be the career girl, to be happy with house and kids. Yet some of the happiest people I know are just everyday ordinary people.

If I feel down sometimes, I think – I'll put my best dress on. That will make me feel better. But it doesn't work like that. When I see people who just don't care, who are so free – they look marvellous. A lot of women don't have that freedom within.

Other people are always telling us what is going to happen so it does happen. They told me I should be frustrated: I became so. They say women are drinking more because of the strains of being a woman today – so this is what is going to happen. The ideas come from the outside, from the media, and then they become fact. The image becomes real.

I *was* happy for a while at home when the kids were there. I liked cooking and sewing in a way – because I loved being the image that I was meant to be. I liked doing what everyone else was doing. I belonged at one stage of my life; it was lovely. But I still didn't know what *I* liked in life. When I joined AA I was forty-two and I had to look back and say, well, I enjoyed English and maths in school. So I did some 'O' levels.

For a woman to find out what she really is, to be proud of it, to believe in it and accept it is the most important thing: just to *be*.

Julie

I remember distinctly the first time I got drunk. I was on a pre-university course in France. I was eighteen. We were sitting in a cafe, about twenty of us, all students. I got a bit pissed – and then just wanted to see how much I could drink.

I puked up in bed that night, in my sleep, and woke up with vomit all over my bedclothes. It was really quite dangerous. But I wasn't appalled by it. I felt it was quite an achievement being able to go over the top. That occasion was my first social encounter with the opposite sex. I was quite nervous and I also wanted to be 'one of the boys'.

Everyone else was going to university after the course except me. I was going to do nursing and I felt a bit embarrassed about it and inadequate. So I didn't tell them at first. My brother – who had been on the course before – made me feel that nursing was for people who were a bit stupid. I didn't really want to be a nurse, but it was that or secretarial – or being a wife.

I had been to a school where we weren't encouraged to do 'A' levels. If you went into the sixth form you did French and driving lessons. I have felt intellectually inadequate from the time I was in school. I was always at the bottom of the class. Except once, when I came third. I felt really guilty about it as I thought everyone else must have thought I was cheating.

I used to drink during that time in France in the same way that I do now – because I have to depend on my personality to make a statement rather than on my achievements.

I also used drinking to stop me from developing the female side. I could become 'one of the boys', and by drinking with men we could be more like brothers and avoid any sexual tensions.

I became part of a group on the course that was more interested in drinking than in going to museums – and we had a whale of a time. I was the jolly, hearty one. Most of the others were boys and I kept up with them socially when it was over.

I was friends with some of the girls too. They were clever. I went to see one of them in Cambridge afterwards when I was nursing and she said to me, 'Are you still washing nappies then?' I felt I was doing a dummy job. It's one of the reasons I eventually left nursing.

I started the nursing course when I got back to London, and drank quite a lot then. It has been part of my reputation ever since. I got in with Australian agency nurses who drank Fosters and we had beer breakfasts. We used to meet at a pub in Piccadilly after a really exhausting night on duty and get pissed.

It was good fun, a good opportunity to act ridiculous. The other Australian nurses were very funny and lively and open. We had a 'what the hell, nothing matters' attitude. It was pleasure-seeking.

Many of the other nurses came from very different working-class backgrounds. They drank Ponys or Babychams in the pub. I didn't feel very comfortable with them.

I had no really close friends at that time. I don't think I knew what that meant. I was ploughing around, always searching for something, without a clue what for. I had no place to settle down or relax.

I also hated nursing. I was very nervous and unsatisfied in the job. Drinking was a way of forgetting about it completely and relaxing. If I had time off I *had* to go out and enjoy myself. I was bored by myself. I needed distracting entertainment.

My nursing training course lasted from when I was nineteen to when I was twenty-three. I lived in a flat with a friend for some of that time. We had a lot of dinner parties and without fail I knew I would be sick from drinking at the end of every evening. It was only wine and we couldn't afford great quantities, but my tolerance wasn't as high then as it is now. I can't be sick now. I drank then because I was nervous and I was trying to appear more capable and social than I was.

After I finished my training I left nursing completely. I drank a fantastic amount then and went to a lot of parties. It was the first time I became quite alarmed at how much I was drinking.

I had met up with an old friend, Jenny, and I was very attracted to her. I wasn't surprised in myself. I knew something was always there. But I had no clue what to do about it – and I felt absolutely disgusted with myself. I was obsessive about her and I had absolutely no one I could tell. I wouldn't dare. So I used to write reams of poetry – or what I called poetry. And I was getting drunk all the time.

Drink is definitely a tool for me. I use it to get things *out*. The more pissed I get the less inhibited I am and I can express emotions that wouldn't be accepted normally. And people say, 'Oh, she's just pissed' – so it's not taken too seriously.

I used it to get over the first step to expressing things I have kept inside of myself, some of them quite positive things. Drink can help make those feelings towards people into a reality. Then it's established, I'm over a hurdle – and the next day I can deal with that reality.

With Jenny I was always testing her out, seeing how far I could go in expressing my feelings without her actually *knowing*. It was totally naive. She didn't understand what was going on. How we managed to maintain our friendship I don't know.

I put on about a stone in weight at the time. I had always been a seven-stone weakling and when I went over eight stone it was the first time I recognized my body. I got more bottom and boobs. It alarmed me – I had always been slightly anorexic. I didn't want to be feminine; the boy in me was strong.

When I was little I was in the Anti-Dust Society. My older brother said all women were dust, and if I wanted to play with him (and there was no one else around) I had to be part of the Anti-Dust Society. So I had to dislike all females and anything feminine. I played with tanks and airplanes, not dollies. I had a little-boy identity.

At the same time a friend of mine was pressurizing me to go travelling with her, and apart from not wanting to leave, I was frightened of travelling in the 'big world'. I really didn't want to go, so I drank my way through until the day we left.

Other people were worried about how much I was drinking, especially my mother. A friend of hers had told her that I would be an alcoholic by the time I was forty if I wasn't careful. I didn't believe it. I knew *why* I was drinking, so I wasn't afraid of becoming an alcoholic, and I could go without drink for some days.

I did eventually go travelling with my friend but I was utterly miserable. I got terribly bad spots which took a year to go away. All the time I was travelling I was sorting out the idea – was I lesbian? I had already made a decision, in fact – which was that I would always be pursuing this question mark about my sexuality. That was why I was drinking.

When I came back I lived in my parent's flat in London.

Whenever they went out, or went away for the weekend, I would hit the gin bottle. It was lovely. I was always drinking *his*, my father's drink. I was getting something back on him.

I was also very careful and scared about replacing it. One time I took two bottles of wine that turned out to be terribly expensive and rare. I looked everywhere for replacements and eventually found some at Justerini and Brooks. They told me the bottles were too young to drink. So when my father took them out for a dinner party I was longing to say to him, 'Don't you think they're a bit young?'

Then for a while I had a job working with mentally handicapped kids. Jenny was living nearby and we met up with a crowd who drank fantastic amounts and spent loads of money. Jenny and I decided to share a flat together and I started being able to articulate my feelings for her.

I talked to her generally about my anxieties that I was attracted to women, and she accepted that it was a part of me. We used to sleep in the same bed, like sisters, holding hands. But I couldn't bear it in the end. I felt very angry with her too. I was drinking a lot to get through those conversations with her. I did make my attraction for her explicit somehow. I told her in a pizza palace that I *really, really* loved her. She understood it but didn't feel the same way. So I had to deal with it and withdraw a lot of the things I had put on to her. She stayed incredibly loyal and supportive.

Then I got so depressed that I couldn't work. I kept getting panics at work, feeling really claustrophobic. I wanted to lash out, to explode. Instead I would sweat and feel very hot. I spent three days in bed smoking myself stupid, on a destructive trip. And then I decided I would have to do something about it.

I started doing psychotherapy. It relieved a lot of tension. It didn't alter the problem, but it made me more able to cope with it. I felt that I wasn't so bad, that I should look after myself more instead of trying to destroy myself.

I moved to a flat in Clapham where I felt very safe and settled. I loved being there and the security took away the need to drink. I went on a vegetarian binge. I was very healthy, but a bit neurotic in a different way – about food. For a year I hardly had a drink.

Then I took a job working with maladjusted boys, which was depressing. They used to pinpoint my vulnerability, asking me about my sex life. At the same time I started a new course of pottery at art school. It was a first glimmer for me; I knew I had a feeling for it and I wanted to do more.

And I was having my first sexual experience with a woman, Jean, at about this time. It was not satisfactory. She didn't want to talk about it and it left me feeling that I still had to go on resolving something. I knew I'd have to have another affair with a woman to sort it out. I wanted to get out of London and out of the relationship.

That was part of the reason why I moved down to Devon to work as an apprentice potter. I had a fairly abstemious time there until I met George. He had come down for the weekend to stay with a friend, and we got arseholed drunk, from Friday night to Sunday. And on Sunday I slept with him.

Drink made it much easier. I felt, if I get pissed I can do this. And we did have good sex for the first part of our relationship. But we always had to be pissed. We never did it sober or in the afternoon. It was always in the dark when we came back from the pub.

We saw each other on weekends for about four or five months, and as I had never felt near to being relaxed with a man I thought – this must be *it*. He had been asking me to get married for ages, jokingly, but I didn't take it as a joke.

I thought – well, why not? I'm getting married. It was partly that I wanted to give a reassurance to my parents that I was okay. I have always seen marriage as part of my future. I can't see myself as being alone when I'm older and marriage seems the only way not to be.

I thought we could live in the village, have children and I'd run a pottery. I haven't exorcized that little fantasy yet. We even set the date and he was going to tell my parents.

But there was something about my feelings for women that

was not resolved and I felt I wanted to see Jean again. I started withdrawing from my relationship with George. We had a terrible row, white anger, and we used to physically fight. I felt suddenly very trapped and wanted to get out. I feel now that I was very unfair to him.

Sex was spoiled. I didn't want him to touch me. When we did have sex I would have to be blotto. I was drinking a lot. I felt he didn't know *me*, he just wanted to have sex with me. It was only partly true, but I focused on it.

I went to see Jean – and slept with her. I felt then that I couldn't carry on with George. All those feelings in me towards women were really much stronger.

The golden opportunity to get out came when a friend in London offered me a place in the house where I live now. That's when I started my ceramics course, and I started going to the Women's Therapy Centre.

I am much more determined now to sort things out. Drinking gives me the energy to face things with women. I feel I have to be hard on myself and steam through things that I had thought a lot about. Drink helps me to do something about it and to talk with my friends.

We have lots of boozy dinner parties in the house. I find I try to get close to people in an aggressive way when I'm drinking. I provoke people to get close to them and establish a relationship.

I always suffer from terrible anxiety and remorse in the morning. I feel terribly guilty about the way I've behaved because I know women aren't supposed to get drunk like that – and angry that it's *because* I'm a woman that I feel so bad.

Usually if I wake up in a really jerky frame of mind it's because I've been talking very personally to someone, usually about sexuality, and gone too far.

There was a time when I had to ring people at four or five in the morning to ask if I had told them something about myself. Especially Jenny – I used to worry that I had told her that I fancied her. I can never remember exactly what happened the night before.

I'm worried that people won't like me any more after I've been drinking, yet I use all the tools - being aggressive and demanding – to make people reject me. I keep doing that. I feel frightened about it. That's what worries me about drink – not that I'll be sitting in a bar till closing time for ever – but simply my potential to be hurtful.

I'm in a new relationship with a woman now: Sue – and we always have a few drinks on Friday evenings. It's a real way of relaxing. But then I go beyond the relaxing stage. I take the lid off my censorship and all these worms that are wriggling around, start flicking out . . .

Last Friday I had an awful row with Sue. I had felt some anger with her, but not to the extent that I expressed. It seems I'm angry with people for my own reasons and not because of anything they've done to me.

But I do feel real anger about having an affair with a woman. She dominates me by *giving*, and sorting things out for me. She forces me to get on with things that I would otherwise put off. I feel afraid of being taken over. I feel like a child.

After nights like last Friday I wake up early with lots of energy. I have to get up and start doing things. I get jerky, things keep popping up in my head. I keep remembering them and feeling shocked. I feel absolutely, utterly . . . uuuugh . . . I can't stand it really . . . really sensing something about me that I don't want to exist. I want to forget it, not face up to the idea that it exists.

The next morning I always say – that's it. *No* more. I must control myself now. I don't trust myself any more not to attack people.

I know that through drink I am testing how much people can take, how much they love you. I push to the limit. In making Sue angry last weekend I found a new level with her. I found limits in our relationship which I have been seeking. In relationships between women you have to shape your own boundaries more than in relationships between men and women, which have rules and limits set from the start.

I enjoy drinking too. You create what feels like devastation and force people to get on to that level with you. It forms a bond that you might not achieve otherwise – which *is* creative. People have never actually gone from me as a result. You feel much closer to people after that incredible writhing around.

Miriam

I have always been attracted to drink. I liked it when the grown-ups drank. They all seemed so much more cheerful – except that my mother looked silly when she got tiddly. After seeing how she behaved, I always forced myself not to show the effects of drink.

Whenever we went out, drinking seemed the thing to do. I wanted to be 'one of the boys' and I used to drink more than the other women. I desperately wanted a boyfriend. I was terribly afraid of people and drink took away my inhibitions. I thought if I got a fella I would be okay – and I did, I had lots of them.

Women frightened me. I was so insecure in my own femininity. I didn't seem to belong anywhere as a woman. I never felt part of anything, and it seemed like everyone else did.

I had a reputation for being a good drinker. People used to call me 'hollow legs'. But I often felt the ill-effects without letting it show. I used to go off and be sick and come back and continue drinking. And I didn't like non-drinking company. I always wanted other people to have one too.

I was married straight from school, because I was pregnant, and I had two children before I was twenty. I had never had a job. I could go weeks without a drink at that time – I was too busy with the children.

Men were more chauvinistic in those days. We had always done what my husband said. He was in the Forces and so we moved a lot. I enjoyed that. I always felt the next place might be the place I belonged to; it might be what I was looking for.

We never lived anywhere longer than two years, by which time

I was always raring to go. I took on a new image each time. I would be the Arty one, or the Hippy one. And as soon as we got established, I wanted to go. I couldn't keep the front up permanently.

It was the same with jobs. They were all just images, not *me*. I had so many images, so many faces, that I lost track of my personality. I had no idea who I was. I once met some people from the drinking scene when I was on my way back from work and they didn't recognize me.

I was aware of how I felt at the time. I had worried about who was the real me from the time I was fourteen. I drank to drown all that.

Then in my late twenties, my marriage broke up. I felt a great sense of freedom. It was the first real decision I had ever made. At last, I had no grown-up appendage. I was on my own and the freedom to drink was one of the many freedoms I had – like smoking in bed. I liked the image, and there was no one to frown and say, 'That's not done.'

I had sexual freedoms too and as many boyfriends as I wanted. But they were baggage for the journey and I felt terribly guilty. I also felt a lot of guilt about my children. Right from the start I felt as inadequate as a mother as I did as a woman. They were both Doctor Spock babies, and I was mostly concerned about the image they created. They had to *look* right. I was always busy organizing them, but it didn't come from the inside.

Drink anaesthetized those feelings. I was like an ostrich; I thought if I put my head in the sand no one would see me. But I used to wake up and worry at three o'clock in the morning.

The children were about seven and nine at the time. They used to think I was occasionally ill, but they say now that they never connected it with drink.

Then I met someone who moved in with us and I started drinking regularly and heavily. I had my first blackout at that time. When I 'came to' I had cooked and served a meal and was getting ready for my son's birthday party. Everything was neat and tidy – and I couldn't remember anything that had happened.

No one else had noticed anything odd about me. I asked my kids, 'Did we have a nice lunch? Who washed up? Who served?' It terrified me and I buried it immediately. Later I turned it into a joke. I said to my boyfriend, 'That was a nice drink you gave me the other day.' The only way I could handle it was to tell it as a funny story.

Then I met the man who was to be my second husband. I liked him because he drank such a lot and was always happy to open a bottle at any time. We seemed a perfect match. But very soon after he moved in it wasn't so good. We quarrelled and he used to beat me. I blamed it on myself. I thought it was to do with my drinking and how I carried on with other men. I always took the blame, and after a while it would always get better. I was terrified of him going and was continually persuading him to stay.

I thought I was really in love. I needed him to direct my life. I believed I didn't know how to cope or what to do without him. But I always *had coped* with bills and so on. Yet once I got someone with a stronger personality, I felt I just couldn't. He organized everything.

Even on our first date when we went out to dinner I said, 'Oh you order for me, I'm fed up with making decisions. I've got too many of them to make.' It was wonderful to give all the responsibility to someone else. I had always had the feeling that everyone else was right and I was wrong.

Then he wanted to move to another flat, because of his job. The children were very upset but I ignored their wishes. He said we *will* move; he had all the arguments – and so we moved.

I was away from all my friends as a result and we were always with his friends. I trotted along behind him, doing everything that he did. We drank a lot and sexually we were 'swinging'. We went to a lot of partner-swapping parties. It all added to my sense of separateness from everyone else. At work I was very prim and proper while my private life was really very odd.

This went on for about five years. I would drink a lot, then take time off work and drink at home. By the time I went to the pub to meet people I was already drunk. The drinking at home didn't count because it wasn't measured. I had no idea how much I drank, although I could have a bottle and a half of spirits without noticing. Then I'd be surprised when I felt drunk after having one drink at the pub.

He was beating me a lot at that time. I had to explain away black eyes and broken bones – but I loved the secrecy of our sex lives. I never blamed him. I hated him sometimes, but I was totally dependent on him. He was my reason for being.

Then he left me, and I was horrified to find out that I hadn't even noticed he had gone until one or two days had passed. The kids had to tell me that he had gone. I was so shocked about not noticing it that I began to think that perhaps drink *was* a problem. Until then I had convinced myself that drink was a good thing; if there was a problem, it was me, not drink.

I decided to go to an AA meeting. It was a great relief to discover there that I wasn't any different to anyone else. Things like wetting the bed that I had been so ashamed of – I used to blame him – I realized that it happened to other people too.

It was agonizing physically but I did stop drinking. I felt so wonderful that I thought – I *can* manage without him. As soon as I said that, he came back.

Life picked up again as it was before, and for the first time I realized just how heavily he was drinking. I felt very superior to him – and to the other AA members. So I stopped going to meetings.

I didn't drink alcohol for quite a few months. I had orange juice when we went to the pub. But one time, when it got towards closing time, I felt so bored that I thought I would have one drink. It gave me a real lift. I remembered that first warm feeling as it goes down. I thought – I've cracked it, I'm fortunate, I can control it.

I did for a while. But by Christmas I was out of control again. His response was to say we had better stop going to all those parties. But I didn't want to stop. I thought it was the good bit of our relationship.

At weekends there would be loads of housework to do. I would open the fridge in the morning to take the milk out, but I would always take a few swigs from a bottle of wine as well. Everything would go fuzzy at the edges. I couldn't do anything then, but I still drank.

Eventually he said, 'We'll get married.' I went along with it. If he had said, 'We'll stand on our heads in the corner,' I would have done it. I had no will-power left.

We got married on Friday the thirteenth, the weekend of the Queen's Jubilee holiday. We spent the weekend drinking, but I couldn't get drunk. I didn't get back to work the next week. I went to bed with someone else when he wasn't there. I thought – that's it. Now I've cocked the whole thing up altogether.

I had thought with the marriage that it would all be okay and there I was, I'd done it again. I told him about it and he didn't mind. He suggested I go back to AA and I said okay. I started going to meetings and stopped drinking again. I was very angry about it this time. I didn't like them at AA. They seemed so straitlaced, po-faced and boring. My life seemed to be stretching out into one long boring tunnel of sobriety.

Everyone at AA was very 'nice', their husbands all went to Al Anon, they had nice' kids. Whereas I had to sneak off after meetings to meet him in the pub. I was embarrassed too when he used to come and get me and everyone could see he was drunk. I didn't know how to adjust my feelings towards him. I thought I had depended on him so much, yet we just couldn't seem to cooperate together.

I used to have a mouthful of his beer now and then, but by Christmas I had more or less accepted that I couldn't drink at all.

We tried to carry on the same life as before but it didn't work. I had to leave him. He cracked up. It was as if we had swapped roles – he was begging *me* not to leave *him*.

I was in my early thirties then. I have more acceptance of life as it is now than I used to. I have found that you can go on being one of the angry ones in AA. Different AA groups have different characters and we are lucky in London to have so many different groups.

I have seen various patterns of women's drinking. Some drink at home alone because it makes them feel a bit naughty, a bit independent. The younger ones who are in professional jobs drink because it's there. They especially are under a lot of pressure.

And lots of women – and men – suffer from the identity thing like I did. You feel as if you are separated from everyone by a big glass wall. It feels as if everyone else has the rule book and you haven't.

I never knew what was 'right' and so it seemed easier to do what was 'bad'. At least I knew what the effect would be when I did the bad thing. I never knew why you should be a good girl.

I felt I had all these inadequacies in me and I chose alcohol to cover them up. I identify very much with my mother, but she gets over her problems with sheer grit and determination. Maybe I couldn't do that as a result of her being so strong.

I think anyone can be a latent alcoholic. It's to do with something spiritual. Anybody successful throughout civilization has always had a spiritual life, values connected to religion, which we no longer have.

That lack of values, lack of self-worth can be disguised by building a huge ego around it. I knew what a shy, frightened person I was but if I told any of my friends they wouldn't have believed me.

Elly

You wouldn't have thought I was a boozer when I was younger. I was a dancer, a member of the Royal Academy. One summer season when I was twenty-three I met the man who was to be my husband. Oh, I believed marriage was totally romantic. I had seen too many Hollywood movies. I thought he would be my slave for evermore, give me freedom, financial security . . . Love? I didn't know the meaning of the word.

My first baby came after I had been married a year, and then my second one. I wasn't unhappy. I loved my babies. We were reasonably well off, we had babysitters, help in the house.

But I wanted to keep up my work and I was offered the chance to do some choreography. But we lived near my mother-in-law and she was horrified at the idea. I felt really guilty that I had such wicked thoughts – a married woman with babies. Good Lord, that should be enough! They made me feel I shouldn't have got married if I wanted to work. I should have told them to take a running jump and done the job.

I didn't really want to have a third baby and I developed a terrible hang-up about sex. Intellectually I knew that sex should be enjoyed, but I was afraid of getting pregnant again. I went to a doctor and she gave me tranquillizers – the heavy barbiturate type – for my 'bad nerves' as she put it. She sent me to a psychiatrist too.

I didn't think I was barmy, I thought I was very *interesting* really. I considered myself an 'artiste' with an 'e', not a suburban housewife. I thought of myself as a martyr, you see.

But I did get pregnant and have a third baby. After that I got very thin, really scraggy. The District Nurse suggested to my husband that he give me a quick tonic of egg and sherry whipped up together every morning. He used to mix it for me – I liked being looked after – and it made me feel, well, I don't know – it's not so bad being a suburban housewife after all . . .

Eventually I started mixing my own, and because I thought I was putting on too much weight I decided to cut out the egg. My husband came home unexpectedly one lunchtime. He looked at me and laughed and said, 'You're pissed.' We thought it was a huge joke. We never realized the danger.

The sherry was the beginning of my drinking, but I didn't feel it was a problem. I was still taking tranquillizers and alcohol. They played havoc with my emotions. I got very high and then very depressed.

I went back to my psychiatrist and he mumbled something

about not drinking alone before sundown, and gave me more pills, purple hearts. Everyone in those days was given them. They made you feel marvellous, intellectual, bright, glamorous. He gave me two a day. I went back and asked for three. I explained I had one in the morning when I sent the kids off to school, one when they came back for lunch, and I wanted one more for the evening and putting them to bed. I still didn't think I was addicted to pills – or booze – it didn't apply to me.

He gave me the extra pills. They meant a great deal to me. I remember sitting down one day and counting them out. Enoch Powell was Minister for Health at the time, and he made a speech about the nation's huge drugs bill and I remember feeling very guilty about it.

I was in one big neurotic mess. I couldn't cope and I couldn't admit it. I had terrible depressions when I came down from the booze and pills. So I was put in a mental hospital and given ECT. That was dreadful, like kicking a wireless to make it go.

But I did like the other patients. There were a lot of other women there who had trouble coping with their families. I liked being institutionalized. All my daily chores were done for me, washing and cooking and cleaning. I still wanted to be a little girl really. My mother-in-law looked after the kids. I think she loved taking my place – I should have realized what was going on.

It was when I came out of hospital that my marriage started to go wrong. We went on holiday with some friends to Austria. We all drank quite a lot then. My husband fell in love with an Austrian girl. I went berserk. They didn't have an affair or anything at the time, but I *knew* he was in love with her. I felt terribly jealous and insecure. I could have killed her – and him.

Let's face it, I was no fun at that time. I was full of pills and booze, I nagged him, I was selfish, wanting my own way all the time. But when he realized he had found my weak spot he started to torment me with this girl – and he was relentless.

I wasn't worried about losing *him*. I was worried about the financial situation. What would I do with the children and no money? It sent me bananas. He told me that he had promised to go back after the holiday and meet her. But when we got back to England he denied it all.

I think he found the responsibility of family life too difficult really. He was totally dependent on his mother who lived very near. She held the purse strings. We were all dependent on her. She had a hotel where we went to eat every Sunday and sometimes the meals were even sent round to us.

I wanted him to be a husband and a father. But he realized that there was no way we could live without his mother. He knew how much emotional pain I was in, but he kept putting the knife in and turning it at every opportunity. I became mentally sick about it. He would leave letters from the Austrian girl lying about and then deny it all. He was terribly cruel.

We had definitely fallen out of love at this stage. I don't think I ever did really love him. If I had we might have been able to cope. During this time he persuaded me that I needed to go to London – we lived in Broadstairs – for a rest. At first I didn't want to go. I knew something terrible was about to happen, but the truth was so painful that I could only glance at bits of it at one time. I wasn't drinking much at the time, just taking the pills.

I went to London and stayed with my family. I kept trying to ring him in Broadstairs but there was no reply. I used to do it from a phone box so my parents wouldn't suspect that anything was wrong.

Then one day my sister came around with a letter for me from Leo, my husband. It was a very clever letter. It said something like, 'As you've always wanted, you can stay where you are in London with Laura' – our youngest daughter. His mother was meant to take the other two girls. There was nothing in the letter about how I was to see them, or the house.

It felt like an electric shock going through me. I was in a terrible state. My family said I had to go back to Broadstairs at once and they came with me. When we got there all the locks had been changed, so I climbed up some scaffolding and through a window and let my father in through the front door. Leo was there all the time. He was in the process of making the house into three flats.

Well, I got a solicitor. I had to get the children back. There were weeks to wait. But I still had this incredible sense of loyalty to Leo! I still thought that something would happen, that everything would be okay.

In court he said I was mentally unstable. I was asked stupid things like – did I let the children play in the road? I said – of course, right in the middle. It was so stupid. Luckily my psychiatrist came to court and said I was okay and capable of looking after my children. I was even beginning to doubt my own sanity by then.

I got a legal separation with maintenance – five pounds for me and five shillings for each of the children. It was 1961 and the divorce laws weren't so good.

There was no drink on the scene at this stage, only sleeping pills. I was frightened, alone in that house with three small children. I didn't even know how to mend a fuse. I bought hundreds of candles and stuck them in every drawer in the house in case. Ridiculous.

Then I became unwell. I thought it was exhaustion, but by the spring I was really very ill. My doctor said, 'Pull yourself together, no wonder you're losing your husband' – that sort of thing. Really, I could crucify her now.

I had TB in fact and had to go to a sanatorium for three months. While I was away Leo didn't pay my maintenance and I had to go to court again. I realized he and his family wanted me to fail so that they could have the children. It was frightening to know that. Next thing was a letter from the Building Society to say he hadn't paid the mortgage and I had to leave. He had deliberately dispossessed me of the house.

It was a dreadful trauma. We had to come up to London and live in a terraced house with no bathroom and an outdoor toilet. It was a big comedown for me. My income was then £12.50 a week. I paid six pounds in rent. I don't know how we managed.

I wasn't meant to work for a year because of the TB, but a woman came from the DHSS and said it was time I got a job. I was furious, I thought I had enough on my plate. But I did get a job, office work at a reasonable salary. We got by. I wasn't drinking. I was still on the purple hearts. I knew I had to make a desperate attempt to bring up my children. I also knew that deep down I wasn't equipped to do it. But with the help of pills I would.

Then one year my union, NALGO, had a cheap drink offer for Christmas. I thought it was a marvellous idea. The previous Christmas had been so painful. It was very shameful being a single mother. I felt the stigma of being separated.

The drink came in November, but by Christmas I had drunk the lot. At no time was I drunk, but it was like putting petrol in a car. It got me started. That was the beginning of compulsive drinking for me. I started to become irresponsible, not paying the bills. I was drinking a quarter of a bottle of gin each evening, regularly. When I went home the kids would offer me tea, but I said no, I'll have a drink. It relieved the tension. I could listen to their problems then and it made me feel better.

But money was very limited and I started to care about budgeting. One week I rationalized that if I got a big bottle, I wouldn't have to go out again. It all went very quickly.

Then we got evicted. It was terrible. I was terrified. I gave up my job as I didn't want them to know about my drinking in the office. I realized that my behaviour was noticeable. I was edgy and unreliable and continuously late in the mornings. When I felt unwell myself I didn't dare take time off because I needed it for when the children were ill. I had to pill myself up to get to work. I was desperate. So I decided to work as a temp, as I would have only myself to answer to. I was kidding myself of course: I knew that when I gave up my regular job I could cash in my pension fund contributions and the money would get me out of a hole – and I could drink more.

At this time Leo, my husband, came to see me and told me that if I took him back to court – to get my home back – he would stop payments to me altogether.

I moved to a half-way house with the kids then. I used to suffer terrible depressions. I rang the Samaritans once and said I was going to kill myself with pills and booze and gave them my children's address. They asked me if I had a drink problem, and I said no, my problem was I didn't have enough money to buy drink. They put me in touch with some AA members who came and took me to a meeting.

I thought that they were lovely people, and if I was an alcoholic I would definitely join . . . I kept going to meetings but I was still drinking very heavily. I heard them talking about alcoholism as an illness and I thought, no, I'm not an alcoholic. I'm drinking because I've got problems.

I was so full of guilt that I was saying it was my fault. I felt I was worthless. I had no self-esteem – but plenty of arrogance.

My kids decided behind my back that they were going to live with my mother-in-law. It was such a blow. I made a serious suicide attempt and ended up in Ealing Alcoholics Unit. I was in for three months. I kept writing to the children but I never heard from them. I used to think, I can get sober if the children come back. But then I realized I couldn't put conditions on my sobriety. I had to learn sufficient self-esteem on my own account.

I stopped drinking. I had to learn to live in the real world without props. If I was rich I would have gone on drinking indefinitely. If I'd married the sort of man I wanted – one who hid the facts from me – I'd be dead today.

Through AA meetings I built up my self-respect. I found the spiritual tone off-putting at first, until I learned not to confuse spirituality with religion.

Alcoholism comes in people, not in bottles. It means that the thought of going without alcohol is unimaginable – even when a doctor gives you pills and tells you not to drink, you can't stop. Both my grandfathers were alcoholics.

My kids drink. It doesn't follow that they're likely to be alcoholics. They've seen what happened to me. They did come back to me very gingerly and one at a time. We have a very good open relationship now. They know alcoholism is an illness, they know I was emotionally immature. I'm not terribly worried about their drinking.

They used to test me by pooling their pocket money to buy a bottle of wine to drink with their beans on toast. After supper they used to mark the bottle and put it in the refrigerator to see if I would drink any. It made me furious at first. I told them about it at my AA meetings and they laughed and reminded me it would take time for my kids to recover too.

I did take my husband to court again two years ago. I wanted a lump sum to compensate for the frittering-away of my assets. I'm fifty-six now and I've got no savings because I kept a roof over those kids' heads for all those years.

He's remarried now and he's very wealthy. He moved to Alderney when I took him to court and all his money was tied up there – so he got away with it. He has sent me a bounced cheque since that's not enforceable.

I think now he's an absolute shit, to be perfectly honest. It's astonishing to think that our marriage lasted nearly ten years. When I saw him in court the last time, I was free of fear because I've got rid of a lot of hang-ups. But he was all sweaty and anxious. I looked at him and felt nothing but intense hatred. Now I've got three lovely daughters, and grandchildren. I've got their love and respect and my own self-respect.

I don't feel any more that I am deprived or inadequate because I don't have a husband. I don't have to be a sex-pot. I can be me. It's wonderful to have come out the other side. We haven't half been brain-washed, us women.

I don't think I am a feminist. There are still a lot of conflicts about women's roles. I didn't really want to go out to work. I was happy with the kids. They used to say, 'We love it when you're home, Mum.' And I don't think a lot of men want to go out to work any more than I did.

I do like men, but I know the man I married was a toad. They say you've got to kiss a lot of toads before you meet a handsome prince, but I don't think I will meet one now. I feel quite comfortable with myself. There is no search any more.

But I do think, listening to women at AA meetings, that their drinking has a lot to do with women's expected role in marriage – and the questioning of those values. Things are getting better but we've still got a long way to go. I have read feminist literature and recognized things in it. I've said, 'Yes, I know that.' Yes, I suppose I am a bit of a feminist . . .

Why drinking is a feminist issue

In this chapter four women talk about the place that alcohol holds in their lives. The details of their lives are very different. The women were born years apart, in different parts of Britain, into differing social classes and expectations. Their experiences of jobs, marriage, money and families are as varied as their personalities.

I approached each of them with a list of questions and each time the list was abandoned as the women started to talk – and answered my questions along the way. To them, it seemed impossible to separate their drinking habits from the context of their whole lives, which is why each interview is like a short lifestory. These women have described their drinking experiences not in terms of when, where, and how much, but in terms of how they feel about themselves, their families, work, relationships and sexuality. And individual as these women are, the same themes emerge from their different accounts.

Each one connects her drinking to the feeling that there is something 'wrong' with herself as a woman, a woman who is unable to fit comfortably into the expected role of wife/mother/worker/lover.

Each one feels guilt that she is not doing what she 'should' be doing, being what she 'should' be, as a woman.

Each woman suffers from a sense of personal inadequacy and low self-esteem which, after the temporary relief of drinking, is lower still.

Alcohol answer to problems.
What it is to be a woman

Drink has offered an avenue of escape from these feelings, and an escape from boredom or frustration with home, work or relationships. Alcohol is also the tool used by these women to fight the inhibitions and restrictions that hedge them about. In Julie's case it has sometimes proved useful, but for the others, it eventually proved destructive.

Each account conveys the same sense of having been through something and emerged on the other side of it after a struggle. Each woman has thought long and deeply about her experience and in consequence her life has changed radically.

But should we believe what these women say? The alcohol professionals are traditionally sceptical of what drinkers say about themselves as self-delusion and deviousness are said to be part and parcel of problem drinking.

It is true that these women have been influenced in the way they articulate and rationalize their experience – most evidently by AA and by psychotherapy. There is a certain repressive strain in AA practice, and the women who have been through the AA programme tend to denigrate their desires and aspirations as unhealthy egotism. Elly, for instance, pokes fun at her own wish to be 'an "artiste" with an "e"'. (See chapter 10.)

Yet these women *have emerged*, sometimes from the prospect of total disaster, and so the terms in which they express their experiences do naturally reflect something of the means of their 'salvation'. I believe these accounts ring true – true to themselves and true to the experiences of many other women I have talked to about drinking – and that women reading them will recognize this.

Each of these women has felt that her drinking was a 'problem', of a more or less serious nature. What, then, have their experiences to do with other women, 'social drinkers' whose drinking has been less troublesome?

The answer is, a great deal. There were times in the lives of all four when alcohol was not a problem. And yet problems did

develop for a variety of reasons – psychological, economic, physiological, social – out of these apparently problem-free times. What
happened to each of them could, and will, happen to many other
women.

There are no definitive differences between 'social drinkers'
and potential 'alcoholics'. Many workers and academics in the
alcohol field now agree that the experience of drinking is a
continuum: we all stand somewhere on it, and differences
between us are largely a matter of degree.

I hope that women who read the accounts of Julie, Jane,
Miriam and Elly will identify with at least some of the things they
say. I believe they are talking about the same feelings which
preoccupy most women, drinkers or not, and that these feelings
have their roots in our inferior economic and social position.

These are personal stories, yet they have a political significance.
Each 'emergence', although very different in detail, follows the
same path. Jane, Julie, Miriam and Elly began their drinking
careers in isolation. Each felt that her 'problem' – whether to do
with sexuality, home, work or marriage – was exclusively her own
and in some way her own fault.

The guilt, anxiety and shame that each one felt, to be intensi-
fied in the vicious circle of dependent drinking, was in part a
consequence of this sense of individual responsibility for 'failure'.

In time, they each came to see their 'failure' in terms of
imposed social expectations about what women are supposed to
be. Having once felt 'wrong' for being 'unable' to measure up to
the stereotypical image of womanhood, they began to question
whether there isn't something 'wrong' with that image. In the
process, they each emerged from isolation, ceased to accept total
blame for their drinking and came to see it in a wider context.
Women's drinking can only be understood in this wider social and
political context.

2

SOCIAL DRINKING

So far, the focus has been on women who ha e felt that, at some stage of their lives, drinking has been a 'problem'. But what of the majority of women who have never been labelled 'problem drinker' or 'alcoholic'?

The women speaking in this chapter see themselves as 'social' drinkers, but this does not mean that their drinking is just a simple social pleasure. Lack of confidence, low self-esteem, boredom, frustration, relief from stress: these reasons have been given for 'problem' drinking, but they are also reasons for 'social' drinking.[1]

Established conventions of drinking and pub-going can also be problematic for women. Women have consistently told me that they feel pressure to drink – but disapproval if they get drunk. Visiting the pub is one of the most popular forms of entertainment in Britain, yet pub life traditionally revolves around men.

Why do we drink?

Most of us drink because we enjoy it. We like alcohol's mellowing, relaxing effect, we like the convivial social ritual of drinking with friends.

> **Kate:** I love drinking. Many of the best times of my life have been associated with drink – either in celebration of

good things happening, or as the result of drink as a catalyst, making things happen.

Drinking is especially important to me as a way of really *talking* with my friends. In a good session over a bottle of whisky all sorts of important things are said that wouldn't be otherwise. It brings you closer to people, creates a greater understanding and intimacy with friends which is tremendously valuable.

I think that women are more creative this way than men. When the men that I know get together for a booze-up the level of their communication doesn't go deeper than usual – they generally don't talk about themselves so much, or about how they feel. For women it seems to be much more an occasion for breaking down barriers and renewing relationships.

And many women, as well as men, look forward to a few drinks as a way of unwinding after a hard day. They regard it positively, as one of the best ways to help themselves cope with the stresses of living in a far from ideal world.

Janet: More than anything else women need to relax. Better to do it on four pints of Special than on a lifetime of tranquillizers.

Lynn: It's a kind of reward. When I've had a really shitty day I promise myself a pint at the end of it. Like yesterday, after driving a hundred miles we were all desperate for a pint. Some of us got really frantic when we thought the pubs had closed at ten-thirty and we were going to be too late.

Sarah: I think there would be an awful lot more suicides in the world if we didn't have drink. Why shouldn't people drink when they have so much to put up with from day to day? I also drink to get things out of myself, a lot of them shitty things that I would like to be able to say anyway, but can't.

Alison: Being on the dole has a lot to do with drinking. Me and a friend were unemployed for about eighteen months. We used to sit at home and drink a couple of bottles of cider a day. We had nothing else to do.

Alex: I would be scared if I couldn't drink ever again. Life would be too bland, too boring.

Diane: I used to drink because I was shy, timid, I had no confidence. I thought I had no brain. I thought I was stupid. Drink gave me confidence to say and do things.

After having children my drinking went down a lot. I had something that was mine. I had love, I had caring. My husband didn't do that for me – to him I was a stray cat that he brought in off the road. Without my children I wouldn't be here today.

But whatever our motives for drinking, and no matter how straightforward they may seem, inevitably we find ourselves entangled with complex taboos and social pressures.

Lynn: It's a cultural thing. The crowd of people I work with go to the pub at lunchtime and afterwards – it's our habit of socializing.

In certain groups you get an image of being a regular boozer. I am the court jester in my group at work. I'm the one who is expected to make everyone laugh.

If I said I didn't want to go to the pub, or asked for an orange juice, there would be raised eyebrows. It's just not the role I play. They expect me to say, 'Jesus, when's the pub open?' – and everyone goes Ho ho ho. It's a sort of Pavlovian reflex, a kind of shorthand substitute for the conversation that dribbles away through the working day.

It's also a way of *not doing* other things. The big problems of the world and the little problems of your life actually don't seem so ghastly when you've had a few pints. You can blather on about them for a while, get pissed, have a great conversation – and at the same time you are not doing anything about them. You are using up time. Its like the song about 'When the pub closes the revolution starts . . .'

But if you don't drink you are a constant reminder to others that your behaviour is really more sensible than everyone else's. Other people who are getting pissed feel a real antagonism if you don't. It's guilt.

Maggie: There's a huge social pressure to drink. You've *got* to have one. It's really difficult to ask for an orange juice, especially with people from work. It's just not accepted.

Sarah: I'm Irish and I've always had a reputation for being a drinker. At times I feel a pressure that I've got to live up to it.

There have been times when I've got drunk from desperation, but I feel happier with my drinking patterns now – except I feel a lot of guilt about wasted days when I drink too much on Friday nights.

Sarah is certainly not alone in feeling guilty about drinking. This sense that women 'should' be responsible about not wasting time has its basis in the prescribed female role of homemaker and child rearer.

Not only is drinking likely to make a woman less efficient as a housekeeper but, researchers argue, taboos against women drinking stem from fears that we will cease to be as sensitive and caring to others as we are supposed to be as mothers: 'There is no doubt that excessive drinking of alcohol grossly interrupts the sensitivity to the needs of others [which] is the essential feature of the second part of the female role – that of child rearer.'[2]

The sexual division of labour and women's traditional role in the family are at the root of social taboos against women's drinking, internalized in us as confusion and guilt.

This awareness that drinking is conventionally regarded as a 'bad thing' in women goes together with a fear of losing control which stops many women from getting drunk.

> **Janet:** The reason why a lot of women don't drink so much as men is that they're frightened of losing control. I'm a teacher and at the end of term I feel I really want to get pissed, just to think of something other than work.
>
> But women have got kids to look after, meals to prepare, hundreds of little things to do. Even for someone like me who doesn't have kids there's always something to do, like the washing or the cleaning. I can't just lie in bed like a man can lie in bed. I've got to get up and do things. I can't waste the whole tomorrow.
>
> It was also drilled into me by my mother not to waste time. She told me that, as a woman, it was an absolute shame for me to waste a day lying in bed with a hangover.
>
> So you don't lose control. You go just far enough and no further.

The strong disapproval of drunkenness affects black women in much the same way.

> **Jean:** Bars in our culture are for men. It is frowned upon for black women to go to pubs; it is seen as the English way of life.
>
> In the West Indies where my family comes from, men go to the bars. But women will drink socially at home. My mother makes punch, often out of Guinness, when we have visitors, but I have never seen her or any of her women friends drunk.
>
> I would be looked down on socially if I got drunk. Men would look down on a woman who drank too much.

> **Marjorie:** The things that once stopped white women from

drinking are still stopping black women. We don't use alcohol apart from socially. It is virtually unknown to us to have 'a good time' on alcohol – we have 'a good time' dancing or at parties. We don't seek release in alcohol either. We bear the problem, or have a moan to a friend.

For a black woman to be alcoholic is a terrible additional stigma. It means you are in a minority of a minority of a minority.

And we can't afford to go around being drunk.

Another factor which puts women off drinking to excess is that being drunk leaves us with lowered defences against harassment.

Maggie: After socializing in the pub I usually have to go home on my own on the tube or the bus. For men it's okay. No one is going to bother them. But for a woman it's bad enough at night anyway, and if your vision is blurred and you're a bit queasy then you are much more vulnerable to being attacked. That stops me from getting out of control.

Being out of control – and not *under* control – has other social dangers for women. 'We don't like our women to drink. They become uncontrollable,' writes a buyer for an off-licence chain in *Marketing Week* magazine. Much of the depression and guilt which all too often come with hangovers stem from a sense of embarrassment or shame that last night we behaved in an 'unfeminine' fashion.

Lynn: The image of the pissed man is very different from that of the pissed woman. The bloke who goes out, gets legless, falls over, goes to sleep on the train, misses his stop and has to walk miles home at three o'clock in the morning is a 'good laugh', 'one of the lads'. He's got a good story to tell in the office the next morning.

Now a woman who does that is not seen in the same way *at all*. It's not a great story – it's a little bit . . . distasteful. It's not a joke. A woman who gets into a right old state and falls over, *she's* not a folk hero. There's definitely a double standard.

Maggie: And, for women, the image of spending a 'night on the tiles' immediately takes on a sexual connotation. For men the reality is just the opposite – they can't perform at all.

In the pub

Nowhere in the social sphere has the drinking double standard been so evident – yet so much taken for granted – as in that great bastian of British social life, the pub.

The Brewers' Society claim that pubs are still the nation's number one leisure industry for people going out. Almost 66 per cent of men go to pubs, compared with 46 per cent of women, according to a Mintel survey.[3] As a nation we spent £16.6 billion in pubs in 1991.

Yet going to the pub is a different experience for most women than it is for men.

Lynn: I feel I'm an oddity – a woman, in a pub, if I am by myself. I need a prop, another reason for being there. So I buy the *Standard*. I hate the bloody *Standard* – but it makes it seem like I've gone in there not to have a drink but to sit and read the paper. I need that prop between me and those men standing at the bar. They're not oddities; they're in their own world.

I like going into the pub at lunchtime for a pint and a sandwich, but in the evening there is more of a sexual threat if you are on your own. To have someone else with you makes you feel more secure. Going in with another woman is a sort of more interesting version of the *Standard*.

This feeling of vulnerability, of being regarded as sexually available, is a common complaint amongst women who drink in pubs – whether alone or with friends.

Linda: I always feel hassled if I go into a pub with women friends. Perhaps the men feel threatened by us. I have a friend who is very sexy and an excellent pool player. When she goes into pubs the men just look at her and say, 'Coooor . . .' They don't take her seriously – until she starts beating them at pool.

Amrit: I never go alone into a pub. The men look at you as if they think you are a prostitute, they all look round, it's horrible. Or they try to pick you up.

Yvonne: I hate waiting for people in a pub. It's a hostile environment. I feel as if it's a man's place to be, and as a woman alone I stick out. It's not just that people will be trying to chat you up, but that they will probably be thinking, 'Oh, poor woman, on her own.'

Stephanie: I just don't feel comfortable going into a pub on my own. I once waited in the toilet for a quarter of an hour for a friend to arrive.

I used to go home to Southend at weekends and go into the pub to see the local crowd. But my confidence would evaporate as I walked in as I always felt other people criticized me for being on my own, as if I had come there to pick someone up.

Perhaps it is because we are often made to feel ill at ease that nearly half of women drinkers establish a familiar pub. Mintel's 1992 survey found that a 'local' is second (after good food) on women's list of priorities.

But it seems unlikely that many women have a pub where they can meet friends and feel at home. All too often women's drinking habits are dictated by the men they associate with. A woman will inherit a new 'regular' with a new man, and when the relationship breaks up she disappears from the scene, losing contact with the whole social group.

> **Susan:** I started going to pubs when I was fifteen with my elder brothers and their mates. I continued drinking with male friends and lovers – in the place which served *their* favourite beer. I have spent up to a year going to a boyfriend's local, getting to know the bar staff, making friends with the other regulars – and then the relationship ends, and that's *it*. I never go into *his* pub again, never meet those people again.
>
> My father thought it was great that I went out drinking with men. It proved to him that I was popular, not a 'wallflower'. And the standard way for any of my boyfriends to get his approval was to bring him a bottle of whisky when they came to visit. He used to say that his main worry was that his daughters would marry dreadful men – the type who wouldn't go out for a drink with him.

Men can have a strong influence over women's drinking habits. Men's heavy drinking often starts when they are young and drinking with their peers. But women's alcohol problems usually develop when they are older – in their thirties or forties – and are often the result of their husbands' or men friends' influence.[4] Women alcoholics are well known to have a greater rate than men of parental alcoholism, and they often marry men with alcohol problems.

But for some women, moving into the traditionally male arena of the pub is an attempt to assert their independence from men and from the home, and a chance to break their social isolation.

> **Sarah:** I love going down to my local, meeting women, drinking and talking. I think it is a real liberation for women to be able to escape from the confines of home. No amount of publicity about the risks of drinking for women is going to make me go back home again.

The Canning is *my* local, not one I go to because my
boyfriend does, which is usually the case for women.

Once in the pub, patterns of drinking are again different for men
and women. Most men drink beer, usually bitter, and drink more
of it than women. Wine, lager and vodka are the favourite drinks
amongst young women, followed by gin, white rum, Scotch and
brandy. Low-alcohol and non-alcoholic drinks doubled in popularity amongst women between 1986 and 1992, while they tripled
in popularity amongst men. But women now drink 3.5 pints of
beer a week (compared to 2.8 pints in 1984) while men drink 9.9
pints a week (compared to 11.6 ten years ago).[5]

Of course there are great regional variations in the social codes
about women drinking, and women in the south of England and
London generally say that they feel more at ease than women
from the north do in pubs.

A 1990 Gallup pole found that while three out of five women
say they can walk into a bar unescorted without attracting
unwanted attention, one in eight women in Yorkshire and
Lancashire still feel that walking into a bar without a male
companion is 'asking for trouble'.[6]

Janet: In the north, women still don't go into pubs in the
backwater areas. A couple of months ago I was at home in
Yorkshire and when I ordered a pint of beer it came in two
half-pint glasses.

Anny: And isn't it ridiculous – the 'ladies' glasses'
syndrome where they give you beer in glasses with stems
like wine glasses if you are a woman?

Elaine: If my mother saw me drinking pints she would be
really shocked – yet it's perfectly okay for me to drink a
double vodka and tonic.

The business of buying drinks, with all its complexities of social
etiquette, is another area of pub custom where women frequently

run into difficulties. If you do let a man buy all the drinks you will probably pay with the uncomfortable feeling that you owe him something, or that *he* feels that you owe him something – socially and/or sexually.

Even when the element of obligation is submerged, the sense of patronage and of the man's superior economic power remains strong. Like the 'gentleman' who opens doors for 'ladies', he feels that he is acting correctly and it would be churlish of you to refuse. You know that he is acting 'correctly' – and that's the trouble: chivalry is all too often a disguise for dominance.

In working relationships, these social codes can be especially stifling for women when a male colleague or boss pays for all the drinks. The woman is placed in the position of guest to the man as host. She feels indebted while he exercises control. In drinking situations with a male colleague or boss who has, at least, the power of hire and fire over her, a woman will find it doubly difficult to assert herself.

More and more women do now pay their own way in pubs – which is not to say they have no further problems.

> **Lynn:** Getting served is terrible. It makes me so angry. You are waiting there at the bar holding out your fiver and a man behind you shouts out, 'A couple of pints, please' – and no problem, he gets served before you.

> **Janet:** And women barmaids are worse than men. They always serve the men first. They look right through me as if to say, 'Go and sit down, dear, this isn't your place, you should be cooking the dinner.' It really infuriates me.

This disapproval of women by women has serious consequences in intensifying the isolation of women with drink problems, but it must be seen in context. It is not surprising that women should absorb and reflect the moral strictures which permeate the dominant – and misogynist – culture, especially since we are the ones that risk the brunt of social disapproval.

Nor is the widely practised round system as fair to women who want to buy drinks as it might seem.

Liz: I never had much money so I used to drink half-pints of beer. But I would always rush up to the bar to buy a round because I wanted to pay my way equally. Then I realized what a good thing the men had going for them: they always drank pints so I was paying out for more than they were.

So I started drinking pints myself to even things out a bit, but I realized that again I had just adopted a male pattern of drinking – and one that's bad for my health.

We need to progress beyond drinking as 'equals' with men in pubs, to a confidence in our own preferences.

Liz is reacting to a dilemma which is increasingly common for young women drinkers. On the one hand, we face a challenge to live up to vague but misplaced notions of equality, keeping up with men drink for drink, buying round for round. But this is not so much 'equality' as *sameness* with men. Equality is far more complex. Women may not *want* to drink so much, we cannot physically tolerate the same amounts of drink as men, and generally we have less spending money than men. Women cannot simply adopt male patterns of socializing when the conditions of our lives are not the same – and why should we even wish to?

Women with children have particular reason to feel that the prevailing customs of pub life do not cater to their needs, because so few pubs make decent provision for children.

Anny: Now that I have a baby, it's a major operation to go out. You have to make sure the pub has a children's room or a beer garden. Children's rooms, however, are rarely as comfortable or inviting as the 'adult only' part of the pub and a beer garden is no good except in summer and at lunchtime or early evening. In Europe, going out is far more of a family thing, but in Britain it's very difficult to go anywhere with kids – especially for women who still have the main responsibility for childcare.

It also makes it very difficult for women to get to political meetings which are often held in pubs.

Janet: My father's whole idea of going to the pub was to get away from the family. He used to say 'I can't stand those screaming kids a moment longer. I'm going to the pub!'

The priorities of men and women when it comes to choosing a pub still differ. According to a 1992 survey by the Brewers' Society what women want most is cleanliness, good service and wholesome food. Ninety per cent of women put clean and comfortable lavatories at the top of their list of priorities. Many women also want clean bars (83 per cent), friendly staff (72 per cent), speedy service (72 per cent) and value for money (69 per cent). Men, on the other hand, are more concerned about getting a good pint of beer.

Pub profits, however, are declining and the brewing industry is facing further losses for the future: not only are there fewer young people in the UK, but many of them are turning their backs on pubs.

In 1990 there were 13.2 million people aged between 15 and 29 in Britain, but by 1993 there were only 12.5 million in this age group. Hence, the identity crisis of the British pub during the 1990s as the trade desperately seeks to target women to recover losses.

'Women now decide where they go out with their partners,' a Brewers' Society spokesman told the *Mail on Sunday*. 'They have economic power and are more mobile.' Pubs across the country have scrambled to appeal to women by discarding their old fashioned image for mock-Victoriana and blackboard menus.

And the pub trade's fight to attract more women drinkers is paying off. The number of women going to a pub once a week rose from 45 to 50 per cent in the first half of the 1990s. (By contrast more men are opting to drink at home rather than in the pub: only 20 per cent of men go to the pub three or more times a week, compared to 30 per cent five years ago).

Another threat to pub profits has come from the rave culture. According to a Henley Centre report in 1993 rave parties are diverting up to £1.8 billion of young people's cash away from pubs every year; pub visits by young people fell by 11 per cent between 1987 and 1991 and the Henley Centre predicts that the figure will be 20 per cent by 1997.[7]

Rave organizers have denied that they are competing with pubs, arguing that pubs are declining because alcohol is no longer fashionable and landlords don't offer value for money. One rave organizer told the *Independent:* 'The recession has made people more aware of value for money. Pubs are hurting because they do not give people their money's worth. They close at 11 pm, offer little in the way of entertainment, and price drinks too high.'

Another organizer believes young people are rejecting traditional drinking environments out of boredom and dissatisfaction with 'alcohol related violence.'

In the early 1990s, an estimated one million young people a week were going to rave parties or nightclubs that stayed open until 4 am or later. Half of them were thought to be taking Ecstasy – which is potentially lethal when mixed with alcohol – and so (most) young people on Ecstasy were avoiding alcohol come the weekend.

Pubs have also been facing competition from bulk personal imports from the continent as people buy cheap beer on trips to France. Since 1993, visitors to France have been able to buy virtually unlimited amounts of beer for personal use at prices which may be 1/6 of those at home. Imports, together with duty free purchases, now account for 15 per cent of all beer drunk in British homes.

And increasingly, as the recession has hit drinkers' wallets, people are opting to drink canned and bottled beer and wine at home, rather than pay out twice as much for much the same drinks in a pub. Sales of take-home beer and lager rose from £2.3 billion in 1991 to £2.9 billion in 1993.

A brewing analyst told the *Daily Mail* in 1994 that 'up to 10,000

pubs could close over the coming years due to government legislation, the recession and greater competition from take-home beer'.
He added that 'women are not attracted to many pubs and influence many of the home sales.'

But some women avoid pubs – and alcohol – altogether.

> **Brenda:** I don't drink. I'm not going to touch anything that
> quietens me down. I want to be really alive. If we were
> allowed to be as alive as we could be, we could kick alcohol
> out of the door.

American feminists have made a film about an alcoholism centre
for women called *We All Have Our Reasons*, which portrays
women's drinking as an explicitly political issue. One woman
wears a T-shirt with the slogan 'Alcoholism is a women's issue',
and in their group sessions the women talk and laugh and cry
about their experiences.

'I drank not to be myself,' says one. 'When I drank I wasn't
myself – that made it okay for me to be alive,' says another, who
had been told for so long that she was worthless that she came to
believe it.

The director of the centre explains that many women are not
allowed by society to be who they really are. This denial includes
our sexuality, and because of this lesbian women find themselves
especially oppressed. 'Women are turning themselves inside out
not to be themselves,' she says, 'especially lesbians.'

The film concludes that alcohol is another 'opium of the
people'. 'If anyone wanted to diabolically set out to keep a people
down,' says a commentator on pictures of down-and-outs
comatose on streets, 'alcohol would be the best possible way. It
pacifies them.'

And the film ends on this note: 'Think about the kind of energy
kept in women by drinking . . . If women were to stop drinking,
think where that energy would go. We could change the world.'

3

A WOMAN'S PLACE

Women have low or no self-esteem; women have extreme
feelings of guilt; women experience much depression;
women, more often than not, must combat their alcoholism
alone, nine out of ten husbands leaving them. There is no
male equivalent to the drinking housewife. Women suffer
not only from alcoholism but from role identification.
Women lack a clear image of their role as women, our
culture having created much of the confusion. Women
alcoholics feel they have failed as wives, as mothers, as
women. They feel guilty because society makes them feel
so. All women live in a sexist society.

*From a letter written by Jean Kirkpatrick, Ph.D., an alcoholic
and counsellor of women alcoholics and President of Women
for Sobriety Inc., to Senator William Hathaway*

Being a woman drinker – alcoholic or not – is, as the women
speaking here have said, a complex and often guilt-ridden business. Women drinkers have already talked about their feelings of
failure – as wives, as mothers, as women – and about the contra-
dictory experiences of social drinking: the desire to unwind or
escape through alcohol, the fear of losing control, the guilt of
drunkenness.

Why does drinking stir up so much confusion and guilt in
women? This can only be seen against the background of what

women are *expected* to be. In this chapter I look at these expectations as they are reflected in the stereotyped images of women and women drinkers in advertising, books, films and the media. The basic 'given' is that we are valued as mates and mothers, and time and time again the drinking woman is portrayed with hostility and/or disgust as a deviant from that role.

Instead of accepting blame for being 'failures' as women, or guilt for our drinking, let's ask whether we accept the stereotyped images of the 'normal' woman which are projected by our culture?

The hand that rocks the cradle

Drunkenness is popularly thought to be much 'worse' in women than in men (see chapter 2). Joan Curlee, an American authority on alcoholism in women, explains it like this:

> Because the role of woman has been equated with the stabilizing functions of wife and mother, the drunken woman is seen to be a special threat; no one likes to believe that the hand that rocks the cradle might be a shaky one. Even among alcoholic women themselves, it is not unusual to hear this statement: 'There is nothing so disgusting as a drunken woman.'
> According to the stereotype a woman who has deserted her feminine role sufficiently to be an alcoholic has deserted respectability in all areas, especially the sexual one. Students of the problem realize that this stereotype is as false as most others, yet it persists.

There are a few examples from history of groups of women who drank heavily. Hogarth's famous Gin Lane print, which shows a child tumbling from the lap of a ragged and dishevelled woman who is drukenly oblivious to its fate, marks one such era. Significantly, gin was called 'Mother's Ruin'. The print is memorable not simply as an exceptional example of female drunkenness, but because the image of a drunken woman is depicted with horror – and inspires horror.

The 'normal' woman

When Shirley Otto, a research psychologist and founder member of DAWN (Drugs and Alcohol, Women's Network), and her colleague Ian Petrie produced a revue for the Camberwell Council on Alcoholism, they chose these three quotations to express some prevailing notions of the feminine role:

> Women are usually more patient in working at unexciting, repetitive tasks. Women on average have more passivity in the inborn core of their personality. I believe women are designed in their deeper instincts to get more pleasure out of life – not only sexually, but socially, occupationally, maternally – when they are not aggressive. To put it another way I think that when women are encouraged to be competitive, too many of them become disagreeable.

> The fact of the matter is that the prime responsibility of a woman probably is to be on earth long enough to find the best male possible for herself, and conceive children who will improve the species.

> To one (woman) belongs the power of feeling, the power of the soul, to the other (man) belongs the strength of vision, the strength of hardness. The man upholds the nation as the woman upholds the family

The first quotation comes from Dr Benjamin Spock, whose influence extended over a whole generation of western mothers and babies. The second comes from the novelist and critic Norman Mailer, and the third is from Adolf Hitler.

Each expresses a stereotype of women – that is, an oversimplified but widely held view about what the typical woman is. They each believe that our role is to be passive and non-competitive, that our place is in the home as spouse and child rearer – and that women are born with these sets of characteristics.

You may not have considered Spock, Mailer and Hitler to have been in the same stream of modern thought, but the sex-role stereotypes which they express are pervasive and powerful, embodying lasting and deeply felt prejudices. One such prejudice is that women are not 'healthy' or 'adult' in the same way that men are. When workers in the mental health field were asked to choose adjectives which described a healthy adult,[1] they came up with words which generally matched their ideas of what a *man* should be. But the characteristics attributed by them to a healthy woman – sensitivity, dependence and self-centredness – were more like those we associate with a child.

And together with this notion of women not being fully adult goes the idea that we are somehow irresponsible 'by nature' – and so in need of control. Bridget Hutter and Gillian Williams have explored the many definitions of what it means to be 'normal' or 'deviant' in our society.[2] They find 'the image of the "normal" woman is . . . time and time again . . . of a person with something of a childish incapacity to govern herself and in some need of protection – a kind of original sin stemming from Eve's inability to control her desire to seek new knowledge'.

The social reality – 'brute inequalities'

This supposed incapacity of women is mirrored in our inferior social position.

The Advertising Standards Authority, in a study of images of women in advertising has looked back to Victorian times and concluded that, until the 1950s at least, the campaign for women's liberation had 'largely secured its aims'. But the ASA recognized that 'formal legal equality' was not enough to confront the 'brute inequalities of the labour market':

> British society asserts the desirability of formal legal equality
> between the sexes, but has not yet assimilated its
> consequences for a labour market which women must enter,
> leave and re-enter in accordance with the requirements of
> family building. In these circumstances equality remains a
> distant goal, the achievement of which must wait upon
> society's ability and willingness to draw out the conse-
> quences of the new relationship between motherhood and
> work which became widely visible in the early 1960s.[3]

Even as traditional a body as the ASA recognizes the lip-service
our society has paid to the idea of equality while doing nothing to
change the structures of the family or the organization of paid
work which keep women unequal. Our expectations have been
raised – and unfulfilled.

On the one hand we feel our role to be changing. In many ways
the position of women *has* improved in recent decades: by 1987
women were two-fifths of the workforce, and the Department of
Employment expects that figure to rise to 44 per cent by the end of
the century. We have more disposable income and more equality
before the law. But men still hold power over women, age-old
notions of women's innate inferiority maintain their grip and the
time-honoured stereotype that 'a woman's place is in the home'
persists. No wonder we feel confusion about what we 'should' be
as women.

Women drinkers: the popular image

In all the manifestations of popular culture – in song and story,
films, newspapers and television – the most misogynistic elements
of the female stereotype become highlighted and exaggerated into
the stereotype of the female drinker.

. . . in fiction: Drunk women and women with drink problems
are rare in our literature, but when they do appear it is in a most

unflattering light. Women as homeless alcoholics received a particularly bad press in both the scientific and fictional literature reviewed by Shirley Otto. There is, she writes, 'no female equivalent of the noble savage portrayal of the male homeless alcoholic'.[4] While writers such as George Orwell and Jack Kerouac portray male down-and-outs as romantic heroes, 'almost no films or books romanticize the female tramp or hobo; such women really do not excite anyone's fantasy or envy'. This is not to suggest that women drinkers *deserve* a more 'romantic' treatment. What is at issue here is the comparative distaste expressed about women drinkers, *because they are women*.

Yet our literature is chock full of romantic male heroes who drink to extinction. Hemingway's hero in *A Farewell to Arms* drinks his way through love, war and hospital, scoring points over an angry nursing staff (Nagging Women) when they find his hospital locker full of bottles.

Raymond Chandler's novels feature a host of hard-drinking heroes whose alcoholic habits are seen as a natural adjunct to their macho personalities. Alternatively, alcohol helps Chandler's more 'sensitive' and romantic characters – like Philip Marlowe – in their struggle to 'bear the pain of existence' and cope with their feelings.

Chandler's novel, *The Long Goodbye*, features two alcoholic men, the enigmatic and misunderstood Terry Lennox and the famous author Roger Wade. Both are portrayed sympathetically, both are rescued from alcoholic benders by the considerate Marlowe, and both are the victims of ruthless and/or 'promiscuous' women.

In contrast, drinking women in the novel are portrayed with contempt and revulsion. The following passage combines some classic stereotypes:

> A small girl with mud-coloured hair and a band around her forehead popped up beside me and put a glass on the bar and bleated . . .
>
> 'Are you interested in Communism?' she asked me. She was glassy eyed and she was running a small red tongue

along her lips as if looking for a crumb of chocolate. 'I think
everyone ought to be,' she went on. 'But when you ask any
of the men here they just want to paw you.'

I nodded and looked over my glass at her snub nose and
sun-coarsened skin.

'Not that I mind too much if it's done nicely,' she told me,
reaching for the fresh drink. She showed me her molars
while she inhaled half of it.

The woman asks Marlowe his name, and starts reciting poetry.
Then she

put her glass down damn nearly empty and closed her eyes
and threw her head back and her arms out, almost hitting
me in the eye. Her voice throbbed with emotion . . .

'You can kiss me if you like,' she said coyly.

This woman is a photofit package of misogynist stereotypes. She is
childish ('small girl'), greedy ('inhaled' her drink), grossly sub-
human ('bleated', 'sun-coarsened', 'molars'), sentimental, crass,
manipulative – and sexually 'permissive'.

Alcoholic women are commonly seen as *either* sluttish *or*
sexless, and there are examples in Chandler of both extremes:

There are blondes and blondes and all blondes have their
points . . . There is the soft and willing alcoholic blonde who
doesn't care what she wears as long as it is mink or where
she goes as long as it is the Starlight Roof and there is plenty
of dry champagne.

These alcoholic stereotypes are *either* sexy, willing and shameless –
or ugly, dirty, animalistic and devoid of sexuality. But both of them
are greedy, as is this woman who blows her nose

on one of the dirtiest handkerchiefs I ever saw. Her eyes
stayed on the bottle. Suspicion fought with thirst, and thirst
was winning. It always does . . .

> Seaweed-coloured eyes stayed on the bottle. A coated
> tongue coiled on her lips . . .
>
> I poured her a slug that would have made me float over a
> wall. She reached for it hungrily and put it down her throat
> and looked at the bottle.

This aura of disgust clings to female drinking characters even
when their portrayal is purportedly sympathetic. Anthony
Burgess's book, *Beard's Roman Women*, has as its central character a
middle-aged script writer. To his dismay, his wife, after years of
keeping pace with his heavy drinking, has developed cirrhosis of
the liver.

> He realized too late what should always have been self-
> evident: that a woman was a smaller vessel than a man, that
> no man had a right to expect a woman, however much a
> woman wished it, to be a real, meaning drink for drink,
> companion.

(There is a patronizing and false assumption that all women
would *wish* to follow the male drinking pattern if we could.) For
some time their life is 'companionate' – i.e. without sex. Her
illness and subsequent death are described in horrible detail with
the emphasis on the decay of her 'former beauty', and on how
repellent her body becomes as a result of the liver disease.

After her death the 'hero' finds himself involved in a string of
sexual adventures with young and 'sexy' women. His wife has
paid for her drinking with her life, while he is released to a fantasy
life of rejuvenated sexual activity and freedom.

Male writers – as characters and as authors – often do have repu-
tations as drinkers which enhance rather than detract from their
images. Figures like Brendan Behan and Dylan Thomas are
legendary for their drinking exploits. Scott Fitzgerald was also said
to have enjoyed the romantic interest which surrounded him as a
'man who drank'. Yet when he wrote to the doctor looking after

his wife Zelda, then in a mental hospital, he blamed her bad
example for his own drinking:

> I gave my wife a comfortable and luxurious life such as few
> European writers ever achieve . . . My work is done on
> coffee, coffee and more coffee, never on alcohol. At the end
> of five or six hours I get up from my desk white and
> trembling and with a steady burn in my stomach to go to
> dinner.
>
> Doubtless a certain irritability developed in those years,
> an inability to be gay, which my wife – who had never tried
> to use her talents and intelligence – was not inclined to
> condone. It was on our coming to Europe in 1924 and upon
> her urging that I began to look forward to wine at dinner –
> she took it at lunch, I did not. We went on hard-drinking
> parties together sometimes, but the regular use of wine and
> aperitives was something that I dreaded but she encouraged
> because she found I was more cheerful then and allowed
> her to drink more.
>
> The ballet idea was something I inaugurated in 1927 to
> stop her idle drinking after she had already so lost herself in
> it as to make suicidal attempts. Since then I have drunk
> more, from unhappiness, and she less, because of her
> physical work – that is another story.

The judgements Fitzgerald makes in this letter parallel those that
Shirley Otto found to be typical in her review of the literature:
that women who drink too much are immature, compulsive,
masochistic, passive, and wilfully destroying themselves rather
than taking control of the situation. In contrast, Fitzgerald justifies
his drinking as a relief from the strain of creativity – drinking in
men is often associated with creativity, talent and self-expression
– and from 'unhappiness', for which Zelda is to blame. The implication is that she has 'driven him to drink'.

And many of the books written about alcohol itself perpetuate the old stereotypes about men and women drinkers. This story is intended to illustrate the dreadful things that can happen when a drinker has a blackout, but the anecdote serves better as an illustration of the deep misogyny which informs our whole culture – and our attitudes to drinking.

> A man wakes up in a hotel room with an appalling hangover to find, sleeping peacefully beside him, an extremely ugly woman. He groans, gets out of bed quietly, dresses, puts twenty pounds on the bedside table and is starting to walk out when he feels a tug at his trouser leg. He looks down and sees a woman who is even uglier than the one in bed. She gazes up at him and says, 'How about something for the bridesmaid?'[6]

The man in this parable got drunk and became the victim of female seduction and entrapment in marriage. It is a warning to men of what can happen when the usual stereotype – of man seducing willing drunk woman – is reversed. His fate is to be married to 'an extremely ugly woman'. (And anyway, 'there's no fun screwing a drunken broad', according to one male interviewee in the same book, 'even if she's your wife'.)

The drunken bridegroom anecdote belongs to a long tradition of stories about men getting drunk together. The earliest recorded stories of Old English celebrate Anglo-Saxon heroes who swilled back the ale while recounting their exploits of fights with monsters, and/or flights with other men. Women make rare appearances in these tales as bearers of drinking cups, or objects of battle.

In medieval England, John Skelton wrote a long narrative poem, 'The Tunning of Elynour Rumming', describing the women who came to drink the brew of Elynour ('sometimes she blends/ the dung of her hens . . .'):

> Some wenches come unlased
> Some huswives come unbrased [undone]

With their naked pappes [breasts]
That flippes and flappes
It wigges and it wagges
Like tawney saffron bagges
A sorte of foule drabbes
All scurvy with scabbes
Some be fly bitten
Some skewed as a kitten
Some with a sho-clout
Bind their heddes about
Some have no here lace
Their lockes aboute their face
Their tresses untrussed
All full of unlust [repulsiveness].

To Skelton's imagination, this group of women drinkers have abandoned all feminine propriety and have sunk to the level of animals.

Yet most of us will have heard boastful stories from contemporary drinking sessions – at sports clubs or stag nights where 'animal' behaviour is the norm. There are few modern female equivalents, apart from the disparagingly named 'hen' party. ('Hen' and 'stag' couldn't be in greater contrast.) In America some younger women have adopted the stag night tradition and get drunk on the night before a wedding. But that the spirit of the occasion is originally masculine is clear from its name – 'bachelorette party'.

. . . in songs, film and television: In songwriting too it is men, not women, who have recourse to the bottle, either for celebration or for the drowning of sorrows – usually caused by a fickle and faithless woman. There are plenty of love-lorn, heart-broken women in popular songs as well, but they don't sing about getting drunk. It is hard to imagine, say, Tina Turner singing, 'Tonight, the bottle let me down,' as Elvis Costello does. Or to imagine the country singer, Tammy Wynette, singing, 'The only time I feel all right is when I've been drinkin',/It eases off the pain a bit and levels out my thinkin',' as the Irish band, the Fury Brothers do.

Nor are there many feature films with a heroine who has drinking problems. In a study of film portrayals of women alcoholics,[7] only one film, *Key Largo*, was found which showed a woman alcoholic as in any way 'heroic' – by the film makers' standards. (I am not implying that it is desirable to portray more women alcoholics in films, or to portray more women alcoholics more 'heroically'; this would only be to mimic the macho pattern.)

These researchers found that films, like books, represented two stereotypes of women alcoholics: 'They are shown either as sluts totally devoid of any self-respect, or as pathetic homeless women.' On the one hand are sexy, cocktail-drinking characters like Mrs Robinson of *The Graduate*. She seduces the much younger graduate who then rejects her 'embarrassing' advances and marries her daughter. On the other is Edna, *The Inebriate Woman*, pathetic, homeless – and sexless.

When Shirley Otto and her colleagues examined the characteristics of women alcoholics in films, they came up with this list of most common attributes, which are, as Otto points out, 'not much different from those traditionally associated with feminine behaviour.[8]

immature (i.e. never leaves home)
tormented
given to forming destructive relationships
passive
masochistic
narcissistic
uses others to escape/be happy
determined
uses her sexuality for recognition, not pleasure
warm
sensitive
exploitable
compulsive
greedy
hedonistic
once beautiful

By contrast, many films portray male alcoholics in a positive, even heroic, light[9] and when – very occasionally– films are made about women with drink problems, they are likely to meet with a horrified reaction like this *Daily Mail* critic's:

> In one field I think women would do well to avoid equality with men. I have in mind alcoholism. There is something formidable and tragic about any alcoholic, but the female variety is really terrible. Nothing more fatally draws attention to this than a film having as its heroine a lush.

In contrast, films like *Animal House*, which shows groups of young men involved in a life of drinking and general debauchery, are greeted as highly comical. Many male comics on film and television get enormous mileage from stories of outrageous drinking sessions. Billy Connolly is famous for his jokes about vomiting drunks (always male). W. C. Fields was a classic alcoholic comedian. Television personalities like Dave Allen have a drink to hand – unimaginable for say, Esther Rantzen. Female characters in television shows are less likely to be witty and jovial as drinkers, than sentimental lushes – like Sue Ellen of *Dallas* (she also has elements of the sexy, 'promiscuous' stereotype) or miserable, desperate characters like Angie of *Eastenders* whose humiliated decline into alcoholism was witnessed by millions.

With the success of *Absolutely Fabulous* in 1993, some journalists argued that the popularity of Joanna Lumley's champagne-sodden character, Patsy, signalled a change in attitude towards women's drinking. Here at last, they claimed, was a lush we could really love. And certainly there is much in Patsy – her rebelliousness, her refusal to worry about 'safe limits', and her sheer enjoyment of getting drunk with a friend – which makes women want to cheer. (It also helps that she is Absolutely Beautiful – despite all the boozing.)

But, as a character, Patsy is a pastiche, outrageously sluttishly, over the top. And as with so much British humour, we laugh because what we see is taboo and – in real life – terribly threatening.

. . . in public and private life: In public life too, a reputation for being a drinker is unlikely to do a man much harm, and may even enhance his reputation as a man of the world who can 'hold his drink'. Winston Churchill was said to be proud of his drinking in the knowledge that it increased his personal reputation and power. The author of a book on Churchill told the *Standard* that

> a lot of people still think he was a heavy drinker, whereas the truth is he was an eccentric drinker. He would have a Scotch and soda at breakfast, yes, but it was a weak one which would last him through lunch . . . He encouraged people to think he consumed large quantities of liquor. It was part of his macho image. But he didn't get drunk.

Churchill was said to have doubted that Britain would ever have a woman Prime Minister, but kept an 'open mind'. Since then we have had a woman PM – but imagine if news got out of Mrs Thatcher downing a whisky at breakfast. It wouldn't enhance her image one bit. Thatcher, by contrast, is reputed to make one whisky last all evening while keeping a stern eye on husband Denis's consumption.

And the anecdote of mutual insult which is said to have passed between Churchill and Margot Asquith shows how easily a man can shake off an accusation of drunkenness. Again, 'ugliness' is his weapon of attack –

Margot Asquith: 'Mr Churchill, you are drunk.'
Winston Churchill: 'And you, madam, are ugly, but I shall be sober tomorrow.'

Churchill is putting down a woman who is telling him off for being drunk, and here we have another well-worn stereotype, the Nagging Woman. Her image is so common that we take it for granted. 'A woman drove me to drink, and I never even thanked her for it,' quipped W. C. Fields.

The assumption is that, for men, it is understandable, natural and justifiable to seek solace from emotional discomfort in alcohol, and that women's unreasonable demands are the source of this discomfort. Again, there is no parallel assumption about women's needs for solace. 'Men drink to drown their sorrows, women drink to revive them,' goes an old saw told to me by my father. When women *do* turn to drink, the assumption is not that we need relief from emotional pain, but that we are drinking from perversity and spite, causing our men embarrassment and shame.

. . . in the news: Today, as more and more women are earning their own incomes, it is taken for granted that we are regular customers in pubs and wine bars. But even now, although it is acceptable for women to have a few drinks, women who get *drunk* still inspire disgust, while men's drinking and drunkenness is seen as far more normal.

In the summer of 1993, the *Daily Star* attacked the 'lager loutesses' who it claimed 'drink and look for fights' in Britain's holiday resorts. Loutesses are described in the *Daily Star* as 'tanked up girls wearing mini-dresses and tight skirts'; the only quote in the article to come from a 'loutess' is, 'I open my legs for anybody.'

A policeman complained to the *Daily Star:*

> Drunken women are worse than men for fighting [in spite of the fact that men cause 80 per cent of pub fights] . . . They [women] kick and spit and are worse than cats. They are a nightmare to arrest: [they] can scratch your face or try to pull your eyes out.[10]

The article concludes that not only are the loutesses 'extremely dangerous', but unlike men they show no remorse for the damage they have done after they sober up. In short, a drunken woman is perceived to be more repellent (violent, unreasonable, unpredictable and sluttish) than her male equivalent.

As Elspeth Kyle of DAWN puts it:

> It is typical of our society to be frightened of women

drinkers – and to license our tabloids to take these attitudes
– when what is really needed is attention for women who
have male partners with drinking problems. A lot of women
are absolutely desperate because their men are drinking –
and often behaving violently.

And in the 1990s another set of 'reasons' for women's drinking
emerged: the increasing pressures of juggling jobs, marriage and
family life. Yet time after time newspaper headlines focused on
only one of the stresses faced by women – paid work.

Some of the headlines are as follows: 'The women who drink to
another day at work' (*Daily Mail* 7 June 1994); 'Career mothers
driven to drink' (*Daily Mail* 18 October 1990); 'More professional
women seeking aid for drink problems' (*Independent* 25 October
1990); 'Drink adverts "put career women at risk" ' (*Daily Mail* 14
March 1991); 'Success drives a girl to drink – lonely high fliers
can't share stress' (*Daily Mail* 25 May 1992); 'Successful women
turning to drink' (*Daily Mail* 1 June 1990).

Much of what was written about women's drinking was
balanced and sensible, but the overriding impression left by the
headline writers is that if only women stopped trying to compete
with men in the workplace, then the problem would be solved.

The journalist Tony Parsons added his bile to a debate about
women's drinking in *Arena* magazine in January 1994. Women
should not drink, he wrote:

Being drunk makes you loud, obnoxious, sentimental . . .
and stupid. There are some things in this world that women
do better than men – shopping, weeping hysterically and
cleaning up around the house – and we should go down to
the pub and let them get on with it.

Drunk women, he argues, are simply no good to men – especially
in bed:

no man wants to go out with a bore or a dead fish. No man wants a drunken woman. They make you ashamed, disgusted and embarrassed. Even more importantly, they make you spill your drink.

To sum up, to get drunk is to be 'unfeminine' – and to threaten men.

. . . in advertising: Advertising is an industry which deliberately uses stereotype images for purposes of profit. Its aim is to create desire in the consumer for, in this case, a brand of alcohol, by linking the brand with images of the 'ideal', the wished-for world.

Images of women as objects of desire, idealized as young, beautiful and usually white are used to sell alcohol to men. And images of sophisticated, glamorous, wealthy women in the company of 'desirable' males are used to sell alcohol to women. Women typically respond to anything that they are persuaded will enhance people's opinion of them.

But advertisers have this dilemma. We have seen that drunkenness is incompatible with notions of the 'normal' female role, and advertisers must carefully skirt the spouse/child rearer areas of stereotyped womanhood to avoid all undesirable suggestions that alcohol makes women, and mothers, drunk.

The advertisers' response is to select certain images of women and to project only those fragments which suit their sales pitch. Whatever is fashionable in modern ideas of liberation is adopted to attract young women drinkers; whatever is 'threatening' in feminism is absent.

The resulting fetishistic images which bombard our conscious and unconscious selves from television and films, billboards and hoardings, newspapers and magazines, confirm both the drinking double standard and the sexual/social double standard:

– Women may drink, but may not get drunk.
– Females 'should' be young and beautiful, objects of male desire.

All revolve around men

Advertisers have even managed to capitalize on the fact that drinking is not as acceptable in women as it is in men. They have taken hold of the status quo and turned it to their advantage by suggesting that drinking is something daring and adventurous, a challenge not to be refused by any young, successful, beautiful and fashionably 'liberated' woman: 'Free the Spirit', say the advertisers of Pernod: 'Be tempted', suggest the makers of vodka in campaigns clearly directed at women. One vodka shows a bright snake coiled around a cocktail glass. This is a glamorous (and phallic) Garden of Eden image of the excitement of the forbidden, the sophistication of knowledge. But it is quite split off from the image of the 'fallen' Eve, chastised and subjected to man's control.

Yet men's dominion over women *is* Paradise according to one White Horse whisky ad showing a tiny desert island covered with the prone bodies of leggy models in black bikinis. One male, a James Bond lookalike with his trousers shorn-off castaway-style at the knees, sits at the edge of the island, smugly sipping his drink.

Complaints to the ASA that this ad was offensive to women were not upheld, but women retaliated with a graffiti campaign, obliterating the man from the picture, painting a feminist symbol and writing 'Paradise' on the all-female island which remained.

Many alcohol ads – like this White Horse poster – identify consumption of alcohol with consumption of women's bodies, a common theme in pornography and in slang which describes women in terms of food – meat, crumpet, tasty.

The only *body* that *satisfies* [my italics] the Grousebeaters' is the slogan of a McEwan's lager cartoon. This depicts a woman in a bikini. Her mouth, breasts and hips are exaggerated. She is supposedly modelling for a painting, but on the easel is a picture of a pint of McEwan's. Two men, pop-eyed, tongues hanging out, leer in the direction of the woman's/the pint's *body*. Again, the ASA did not uphold complaints that this advertisement was offensive to women.

* * *

Women are increasingly important as consumers in the drinks market, and advertisers have appropriated fashionable notions of 'women's lib' to sell traditionally male drinks to women: 'Why should men have all the serious drinks?' begins a Lowenbrau Pils advertisement:

> It has long been an unfortunate tradition that while men cooled themselves with a refreshing beer, the ladies sipped sticky green drinks with cherries . . . And if you did want a more sensible drink you were limited to lagers or halves of bitter.

The copy is illustrated by a picture of a young, slim, sophisticated woman sipping from a stemmed, half-pint glass. The advertisement pretends to debunk the old-fashioned 'sipped sticky green drinks' stereotype but has merely updated it. And the woman's image suggests that you can drink (high-alcohol) beer without getting fat and without being 'unfeminine'.

The copy continues in an arch, conspiratorial tone – Lowenbrau's brewing process takes place

> exclusively in Bavaria . . . as the men will confirm. (Being very surprised that you know more about Pils than they do!) . . . And while they (the German brewers) know that men are critical of beer, they know that the ladies can be positively withering. So Lowenbrau Pils has been brewed very much with that in mind. Because the Germans take their women even more seriously than their beer.

The flattery is supposedly directed at women's superior judgement and criticism. But it consists of patronizing suggestions that 'ladies' are 'equal' to challenging male expertise on beer, reducing the concept of equality to the most banal level.

Not all advertisements for alcohol are as blatant as this in their manipulation of stereotyped feminine roles. I studied the ASA's file of advertisements for alcohol which appeared in the print media in the year leading up to December 1993. Of a total of 259 advertisements, the great majority used images which were not overtly sexual.

But of the remainder which did use directly masculine/feminine imagery the most common technique was to associate alcohol with sexual attractiveness and success in finding a desirable mate.

'Go For Gold', says a Ballantines Gold Seal whisky advertisement, showing a blonde female figure, coquettishly draped, lying down. 'After dark, Tia Maria', suggests the advert for this liqueur, with an image of a glamorous black woman.

In the 1990s whisky advertisers also began to target women, aiming at a new and lucrative market. 'Unmistakeable spirit' reads one Irish Mist advertisement, which shows three young women giggling at a table in a wine bar. The two young men who can be seen at the table next to them are clearly eyeing them up and planning their move. The message is that a sophisticated, whisky drinking woman is attractive to men (as long as she is not obviously drunk).

Idyllic coupledom is the theme of a number of other advertisements from this collection. In a series of advertisements for Californian wines, the copy suggests happy romantic holidays: 'The city he loved. The café she remembered', (against a picture of San Francisco); 'The view he remembered. The food she'd prepared', (the image is of the beach Big Sur).

Another advertisement, from Cointreau, directly links alcohol with sexual allure. 'The second thing he noticed was that she was drinking Cointreau' runs the copy, illustrated by no more than a pair of women's legs.

On the other hand, alcohol is as good as sex – if not better – suggest several advertisements. 'The path of true love never runs like this', according to the Jameson advertisement, claiming 'exceptional smoothness' for its brand of whisky.

'You didn't think a whisky could contain so much pleasure?', asks an advertisement for The Macallen whisky, suggestively depicting a big-bottomed horsewoman wielding a riding whip under the slogan, 'Why be afraid of Coming First?'

In 1993, however, only one alcohol advertisement was investigated by the ASA after complaints that it contravened advertising rules by linking alcohol with sexual attractiveness. This was a whisky advertisement which showed a woman standing on a bar table in a miniskirt and fishnets, while below her stood a man – looking up.

Pairing off with a man is the bait of all the advertisements aimed at women. Strikingly, there are *no* advertisements in this collection which appeal to women on any other basis. Their message conforms to the Norman Mailer stereotype – but only in part. Woman is on earth 'to find the best male possible for herself'. However, there is no mention of the second part of her stereotype function – to 'conceive children who will improve the species'. This is reserved for the advertising of other products such as headache tablets and tranquillizers, in which women are portrayed as exhausted, harassed and 'neurotic' housewives and mothers.

In contrast, the majority of advertisements which are aimed at men (still the chief consumers of alcohol), do not take pairing off as their main theme. Symbols of 'the good life' predominate: golf-courses, cocktail bars, airport lounges, forests, stags and luscious illustrations of the bottle. They represent the conventionally 'manly' pursuits (sport, rugby, hunting); they suggest affluence, strength, virility, or simply the pleasures of drinking.

Stereotyped ideas of men are being used here, just as they are of women, but the implications are entirely different. They suggest that men have a far wider range of interest and greater power in the world than women, and have more to do than simply find a suitable mate.

The effects of all these images on our lives as women and women drinkers are many and complex.

On one level, impossible to measure, is the effect on women's self-image and self-esteem. The constant reiteration of the themes that women 'should' be young and beautiful – while at the same time maintaining our primary role as spouse and child rearer – implies that those who don't fit that image and this role are inadequate as women. It also encourages the perception of women as objects, and reinforces sexist assumptions and behaviour. In previous chapters, women have talked about how the resulting negative feelings about themselves can lead into the downward spiral of problem drinking – a devastating illustration of what happens when we internalize images of ourselves, and judge our 'success' or 'failure' in relation to them.

These images also have a negative effect on public attitudes to women's drinking and drunkenness. For as long as the stigma against women's drunkenness persists, women will feel especially guilty about their drinking and will be reluctant to come forward for treatment. The consequences for women's health and well-being are severe.

Furthermore, public attitudes, shaped by these stereotypes, can affect the treatment of women with drink problems so that their chances of recovery are undermined.

In a 'brainstorming exercise' with colleagues in the alcohol field, Shirley Otto came up with this list of adjectives which the participants thought described lay and professional attitudes to male and female alcoholics:

Female alcoholics	Male alcoholics
mad	mad
depressed	sad
ugly	bad
difficult	dirty
demanding	aggressive
wilful	charming
passive	alienated
manipulative	artistic
cunning	unemployed

The adjectives applied to women are without exception negative, and almost all imply moral failure or personality 'defects'. But the words applying to men are less negative – or even positive (i.e. 'charming'), and some of them – 'alienated', 'unemployed' – imply that in the man's case force of circumstances is to blame rather than moral inadequacy.

There is also evidence that women with drink problems are shielded longer than men by their families and GPs, and that women seeking treatment find it more difficult to obtain. And when women are treated for drink problems, they are more likely than men to be treated as *mentally* ill.

One survey which assessed attitudes of workers in the field to treatment, found that 'cultural preconceptions as to appropriate male and female behaviour operate in ways which handicap women. The belief that women's alcoholism is more difficult to detect is matched by a concomitant belief that their alcoholism is somehow more pathological than men's.'

In effect, this means that 'women's chances of receiving psychiatric treatment once their alcohol problem is acknowledged is one in four, whereas men's are only one in six'. And 'women pass through many initial difficulties before they get treatment'. On average, according to the report, women had to wait seven years between the time they first asked for help and the eventual referral for help.

The survey showed that prejudice against women's drunkenness handicaps women in the following ways: 'It was more difficult to identify alcoholism in women . . . Women were more reluctant to admit their condition, and . . . there was more stigma attached to females as opposed to males.'

Sex-role stereotypes are so pervasive that they, like other deeply held prejudices, have taken on the weight of common 'truths'. Moral rightness or wrongness is tied up in conformity to widely accepted social norms.

But definitions of male and female in our culture, and of men and women as drinkers, do damage to both. When the image of what we 'should' be does not fit with what we feel ourselves to be, the result is confusion and guilt: 'If a woman does not behave "normally" then questions are asked about her hormones . . . or her "poor relations" with her father . . . not whether there is something wrong with the identikit picture of the normal woman.'[11]

4

THE POLITICS OF ALCOHOL

Women are drinking more, and more women are suffering from alcohol-related harm as a result.

But this increase must be seen in the context of economic factors – price, income and availability – which encourage us to drink more, and political factors – governmental collusion, parliamentary apathy, huge industrial vested interest, lack of public education – which are doing nothing to stop the increase in drinking. And in the 1990s the pressures on women are greater than ever. The undermining of the NHS, cuts in benefits and social security provision, the dearth of care for children and the elderly, the need to earn a living as well as running the home: all these factors are piling stress on women who may well turn to alcohol as a form of relief or self-medication.

The question must be asked: why is our society pushing us to seek chemical 'solutions' to our problems? Alcohol *temporarily* lifts depression, reduces anxiety, numbs loneliness and boredom. It helps, temporarily, to make life more bearable – but encourages us to suffer rather than resist.

The answer to the question has to do with the nature of capitalism and the profit priorities of our governments and industrialists.

Women are drinking more

Drinking in Britain is at its highest level for over half a century (following a sharp decline from still higher nineteenth-century levels),[1] and during the 1970s women's rates of consumption roughly doubled.[2] In the twenty years up to 1977, beer drinking in the UK increased by 44 per cent, consumption of wine went up by 265 per cent and our consumption of spirits more than doubled to 119 per cent. Sales of spirits rose 114.5 per cent during the 1970s, with vodka, gin and white rum – amongst women's favourites – showing the biggest increase.[3]

In 1992 11 per cent of women aged 18 and over were drinking more than the recommended sensible maximum amounts of 14 units a week compared to 9 per cent in 1984, while 2 per cent were drinking more than 35 units a week – a level which doctors consider to be definitely dangerous to health.[4]

The rate of increase in women's drinking, and the consequent rate of increase in our drinking problems, is growing faster than men's. Health statistics show that more and more women are seeking treatment, becoming ill and dying as a result of drinking. And this rise is in spite of women's traditional reluctance to come forward for help with their drinking problems.

The trend for women to drink more is a continuing phenomenon. In the years between 1930 and 1971, the proportion of young married women who drank regularly rose from 24 to 91 per cent.[5] And these days women are starting young: a 1991 study from Edinburgh showed that 96 per cent of girls aged 14 to 16 regularly drink alcohol.

The number of women diagnosed as dependent on alcohol trebled between 1964 and 1975 (while the numbers of men doubled), and deaths from cirrhosis rose by 40 per cent in women between 1979 and 1989. According to DAWN (Drugs and Alcohol Women's Network), six times as many women are dying of cirrhosis as did at the beginning of the 1970's. The proportion of women to men being treated in mental hospitals for alcoholism shot up from one quarter of the total in 1960, to about one half by 1980. Between 1979 and 1986 there was a 23 per cent rise in the number of women admitted to mental illness hospitals with a diagnosis of alcohol misuse (compared to a 17 per cent rise for men).[6]

Over 25,000 deaths a year in Britain are attributed to alcohol: 10,000 of these are of women. Nine out of ten women suffering from severe alcohol problems are abandoned by their husbands, and women drinkers often lose their families as well as their jobs and their homes.

DAWN says that in the early 1970s the ratio of females to males seeking help was one in eight. By the 1990s the ratio was at least one in three. Female membership of AA increased from one in five members in 1972, to one in three in 1981.[7] The latest (1991) figures from AA still show that women are 36 per cent of members.

More women are getting into trouble with the law over drinking. Although there are still many more male than female drunken offenders (only about eight in a hundred are women) the *rate* of increase in drunken offences has been seven times greater amongst women; between 1973 and 1983 female drunken offences rose 22 per cent, as opposed to 3 per cent for men.[8] Fifty per cent of women in prison in the 1990s are estimated to be problem drinkers. Women have also been a minority in the drunken driving statistics, numbering only one in a hundred offenders when the breathalyser was first used to test this in 1968. But in the following decade, the rate of convictions for women drunk drivers rose to 3 per cent, while male offences declined,[9] and between 1975 and 1985 the rate for women's convictions rose by 225 per cent. By 1991 women were 7 per cent of offenders.[10]

It is possible that some of these statistics can be explained by factors other than changes in our drinking habits. For instance, the increased numbers of women coming for treatment could be seen as a reflection of a lessening stigma around alcoholism. But, taken together, the evidence of these figures is overwhelming – there is little doubt that there has been a real and serious rise in women's drinking.

According to Alcohol Concern (*Women and Drinking*), the vast majority of women are 'extremely moderate drinkers'. Over 90 per cent drink less than 15 units, and 70 per cent drink less than 5 units a week. However, women's drinking in the 35–44 age group went up by a third in the decade after 1978. Women of this age who previously drank on average 4.6 units a week, increased their consumption to 6.1 units.[11] And for women (in contrast to men), the higher their income, the higher their alcohol consumption. According to the latest General Household Survey (1992), 15 per cent of professional women drink more than the recommended safe limit, compared with 8 per cent of women in unskilled manual jobs.

Young women, with free time and money to spend, are also drinking more. Alcohol Concern say that 45 per cent of 'heavy-drinking' women are aged under 25 and unmarried. These are likely to be women without the constraints of partners and children, and who have jobs and an active social life.

Little is known about drinking amongst women from the ethnic minorities. There are some, mainly Muslim cultures, which don't drink alcohol. In others, such as the Afro-Caribbean community, alcohol has always been cheap and readily available and heavy drinking is not perceived as a problem. Many Afro-Caribbean women drink on special occasions such as parties and weddings. According to the DAWN booklet 'Black Women and Alcohol' this may mean that some women are damaging themselves through binge drinking – even if they do not drink regularly.

According to a study of black women and dependency by DAWN (1987), there is general acknowledgement in the drug and alcohol field that services are not meeting the needs of the black community. Despite the fact that black women have been in this country for many years, there have been few attempts to look at their use of alcohol or provision of services for those who develop problems. DAWN put it as simply as this: 'black women do not present for help'.

The DAWN study found that the vast majority of black women had no knowledge of safe levels of drinking and that many were drinking well in excess of the 'safe' limit for women. And in another DAWN study (*London Survey of Facilities*, 1986), 12 per cent of women thought they might have a drink problem. But only one in ten of these had sought help from an alcohol agency.

In DAWN's 1994 survey of drug and alcohol services for women, it emerged that only 7 per cent of agencies reported providing specific services for black (African, Caribbean and Asian) women, while 4 per cent provide a service to other cultural groups.

Nearly half of the women interviewed by DAWN said they did drink alone – often an indication of a drink problem or future problem. The same number said they drank at parties. Although the number of black women drinking in pubs has risen over the last few years, it is still rare to see a black woman in some pubs.

But the great majority (78 per cent) felt that black women are under pressure to drink, because, as one woman put it: 'Black women find themselves under strain from all angles – relationships, in the job market, politically. It affects us more being black and women, trying to assert our equal rights in every situation.'

In America, fewer black women than white women drink, but among those who do there is a higher percentage of heavy drinkers.[12]

And studies in America have found that lesbian women experience a 'much higher rate of alcohol problems than heterosexual women'.[13] Factors contributing to this are isolation, alienation and fear – undoubtedly consequences of society's negative attitude to lesbianism.

DAWN concluded in 1994 that in terms of help for drinking problems, 'the levels of service available to black and ethnic minority women, lesbians and women with disabilities remain disappointingly low.'

Economic reasons for the increase in drinking: People drink more when alcohol is more available to them, both in terms of outlets and of price (see below). And alcohol has become more available to women on both counts.

Alcohol has been getting cheaper while women have been earning more money. Many of women's jobs have been in the service sector and are low paid and/or part-time, but women have gained more control over their expenditure.

In the latter half of this century the real price of alcohol has also fallen. It has been estimated that in 1950 a manual worker would have had to work twenty-three minutes to earn the price of a pint of beer, and nine minutes for a large loaf of bread. But by 1976 he would only have had to work twelve minutes to earn the pint, and eleven minutes to earn the equivalent loaf.[14] By 1990 a woman office worker could earn the price of a bottle of whisky in 2.2 hours: in the mid-1960s it would have taken her 7.2 hours.[15] ACCEPT (Alcoholism Community Centres for Education, Prevention and Treatment) have calculated that between 1967 and 1977 the real price of beer fell by 4 per cent, the real price of wines by 14 per cent, and the real price of spirits by 21 per cent. This means that the drinks most attractive to women – wines and spirits – fell most in real price. In real terms, alcohol is still cheaper than it was in the period before the Second World War.[16]

Alcohol has also become easier to buy. During the 1960s the laws changed to allow off-licences to open during normal shopping hours, and grocery chains and supermarkets began to open drinks departments. By 1977 half of Britain's supermarkets had licences to sell alcohol and it became 'much easier, more impersonal, and more "respectable" for women to obtain alcohol at a supermarket than it had been in pubs and even in off-licences.

By 1980 women had become more important than men for the bulk of purchases from licensed stores.[17] In 1988 the law was changed to allow longer opening hours for pubs. And more restaurants, sports centres, theatres and even cinemas are being granted liquor licences.

And as women have become more important as consumers, the advertising industry has invested many millions of pounds each year in persuading women to drink more. Some £200 million each year is spent on advertising alcohol, and a large percentage of this goes on advertising drinks which are attractive to women, such as wines and spirits. Even the advertisements for Guinness – traditionally a man's drink and a virility symbol – changed to attract women drinkers.

Advertising has helped make drinking more fashionable for women with its huge campaigns to convince us of the glamour of whisky and the sophistication of vodka. And for their part, the brewers have invested large sums in the redecoration of pubs, partly to make pubs more attractive to women.[16]

Yet at the end of the 1980s came signs that the Advertising Standards Authority and the Independent Broadcasting Authority were changing their attitudes. In December 1988 the ASA tightened up their guidelines, followed by the IBA in March 1989. Their new, tougher codes attempted to restrict advertising targeted at young people, by banning actors under twenty-five for instance.

But pressure groups claimed these were cosmetic changes, and of thirty complaints put in to the ASA by GLAAS (Greater London Association of Alcohol Services) not one was accepted.

Cheaper alcohol – more drinking – more alcohol abuse

These two areas of change in our drinking – the increase in availability and the increase in alcohol-related problems – are closely linked in a way that has vital implications for the policies and politics of alcohol.

First of all, it's no longer a matter of dispute that increased availability leads to increased drinking. Changes in legislation and in general economic conditions have probably been the major cause of the dramatic increases in consumption that have taken place throughout the world in recent decades. And there are plenty of historical examples which show that changes in the law affecting price and availability can alter social attitudes to drinking and our drinking habits – in either direction.

During the sixties, when the developed nations became more prosperous, drinking increased rapidly; it also increased most in those nations whose standard of living showed the greatest rise. This increase coincided with a general drop in the real price of alcohol and a lessening of controls on its sale.

After a late-nineteenth-century high, levels of British drinking sank when licensing and other controls were imposed in 1915 and 1916 – with the aim of boosting the war effort and munitions production.[19] Consumption stayed at this lower level (as did alcohol-related harm such as death from cirrhosis) for as long as alcohol stayed relatively expensive – until the early sixties. Since then, however, we have been returning to the higher, turn-of-the-century levels of drinking (and alcohol-related harm), and consumption more than doubled in the last three decades.[20] According to Alcohol Concern ('Find Out About Drink', 1988) the average Briton drank 3.7 litres of pure alcohol in 1950, but by 1980 the figure was 7.8 litres.

The second vital factor in this scenario is that, without doubt, increased consumption in a population leads to an increase in the numbers of people who will suffer from drink problems. This close relationship has been expressed in the 'Ledermann hypothesis', named after the researcher who claimed that if the average consumption of a population is known, the proportion of that population at risk of harm can be calculated from that figure.[21]

And it is widely known that other alcohol-related problems rise when consumption rises. Studies in the UK, Canada, the USA and other countries have shown that the rates of death from cirrhosis are so closely linked to the amount consumed in a population that it is possible to work out a country's consumption from its cirrhosis figures.[22]

Implications for dealing with alcohol problems

These factors have important implications for our definition and treatment of alcohol problems. When 'alcoholism' is considered a 'disease', as it has been in recent years (see chapter 6), responsibility for treating it and recommending its control becomes the responsibility of the medical profession. But it is now generally accepted that a person develops alcohol dependency as a result of drinking too much for too long, rather than as a result of personality or biochemical factors, and that people do drink more and so develop more problems when alcohol becomes more easily available. Alcohol problems then are, to a large extent, the creation of the alcohol industry, the alcohol lobby and the politicians who regulate the availability of alcohol.

Of course, the medical profession has a large part to play in the treatment of alcohol problems, but, as R. E. Kendall puts it, 'the medical profession and the caring professions in general are just as incapable of dealing effectively with the harm and suffering caused by alcoholism as the medical services of the Armed Forces are incapable of dealing with the harm and suffering caused by war'.[23]

The annual health and social costs of alcohol abuse total between £2 billion and £10 billion, say Alcohol Concern (in *Why Alcohol Concern?*, 1990).

They also say that:

– One in six accident and emergency cases in hospitals is alcohol-related.

– Industry loses up to 14 million days a year through absenteeism after drinking.

– A violent crime under the influence of alcohol is committed every eight minutes.

A report in *The Times*[24] revealed that: – 28,000 people lose their lives in Britain each year because of alcohol. The causes of death range from drinking and driving, to suicide, cirrhosis of the liver and alcohol overdoses. – The cost to industry amounts to more than £2 billion a year in terms of alcohol-related sickness absence, reduced efficiency, accidents and other losses.

According to the Health Education Authority, alcohol-related deaths among women have risen sixteen-fold since the early 1960s. In 1988, 1,386 women died as a result of heavy drinking (i.e. from cirrhosis, alcohol dependence syndrome and poisoning).

Figures from Al-Anon (1989) show that one in twelve Britons is adversely affected by problem drinking. And as many as four million people in the UK and Ireland are seriously affected when someone close to them has a drinking problem.

Alcohol is also thought to be implicated in a third of all child abuse cases. In addition, it is a significant factor in violence against women.

Nearly half of women interviewed in a 1992 study by Alcohol Concern strongly agreed that 'alcohol is an important factor in violence in the home,' and a further 39 per cent partially agreed with this statement. Research indicates that women with alcohol problems have experienced high rates of violence during their childhoods and as adults.[25]

What then, in the face of the huge increases in alcohol problems, are the politicians doing to improve the situation? At present the answer is – worse than nothing. A series of major reports[26] in the 1970s and 1980s recommended that the government should control the alcohol supply in the health interest by applying fiscal measures, but instead the rates of alcohol consumption have been allowed to go on rising in the interests of government revenue and drinks trade profits.

A Think Tank (Central Policy Review Staff) study[27] which reported the huge rise in drinking in recent years also predicted further increases in consumption. It made major recommendations: that the tax on drinks should be linked to the retail price index, that there should be more licensing restrictions, tougher drink-driving laws, an investigation into the effects of drink advertising, and a new Advisory Council on Alcohol Policies – none of which have been implemented by the government.

In fact, the government never published the report (it was subsequently published at Stockholm University), and instead the DHSS produced *Drinking Sensibly*, a booklet which the *British Journal of Addiction* called 'flagrantly misleading' and described as 'halfway between a distasteful joke and an obscene publication … [Its] essential policy position is that the health of the people is an optional extra.'[28]

Drinking Sensibly did outline the effects, causes and costs of alcohol misuse in this country, all of which should point to the need for action to control price and availability. But when it considered 'Economic Implications' the apparent concern with our toll of disease and death was superseded by a prior consideration – profit: 'A further consideration in setting alcohol duties primarily to serve health and social ends is that this would reduce their value to the government as flexible instruments for *obtaining revenue* [my italics] and for wider economic policy.'[29]

In short, successive British government have refused even to put problem-drinking on the political agenda. It has been judged sufficient to tell people about safe drinking levels through health education programmes – and then to leave it up to the individual.

Meanwhile, the agencies who provide our scarce alcohol services estimate that at least £25 million is needed to ensure that every area in the country has some kind of adequate scheme on top of existing provisions. The UK currently has a tenth of the rehabilitation facilities of West Germany although our levels of drinking problems are comparable.

Vested interests: To reduce the damage from alcohol, the country must consume less alcohol, but this reduction would be directly in conflict with the interests of the government, politicians and the drinks trade.

As a nation we spend £1.87 billion on beers, ciders, wines and spirits every year (1988 figures). The taxes (excise duties plus

VAT) which go to the government from drink were nearly double this figure in 1988. In addition, Britain has a healthy balance of trade in alcohol: in 1992 our exports were nearly double our imports.[30]

There is also a lot at stake in the drinks trade in terms of employment. In 1992, 1,036,000 people were employed in brewing and related industries in Britain.

The drinks industry is powerful and efficient; its large profits have been ploughed back into new production and distribution facilities. The companies that produce alcohol are enormous and have many other interests. By 1980 the five biggest breweries were among the 126 top companies in the UK.[31] The drinks industry has great political influence and in 1979 it donated at least £107,945 to the Conservative Party and its associates.[32]

Alcohol is also one of the largest sources of revenue to the advertising industry. Some £200 million a year is spent on advertising and promoting alcohol. The media also benefit from the coverage of the many sporting activities sponsored by the drinks industry.

Interests within the government have been widespread and conflicting; in the early 1980s, sixteen governmental departments had some interest in alcohol[73] and the government had no coordinated approach to alcohol problems. The Department of Trade wanted to maintain the high levels of employment in the industry, while the Department of Health was pulling in the opposite direction. And in that most powerful of government departments, the Treasury, the main concern has been that huge revenues from alcohol should not fall.

The apathy of Parliament in acting on alcohol problems is in part explained by the fact that, as the Conservatives began their long rule over Britain in 1979, a staggering one in ten MPs had vested interests in alcohol. The alcohol lobby in the Houses of Parliament 'is larger and better supported than even the tobacco lobby', wrote Mike Daube in the *Times Health Supplement* in 1981. 'The disturbing difference is that the alcohol lobby has not yet been wheeled into action: there is no need – its ascendency in Parliament is broadly accepted, and has scarcely been challenged.'[34]

In 1981, thirty-four MPs had a 'direct financial interest' in the drinks industry (i.e. those MPs with a 'clear financial link with the drinks industry or with a major advertising or PR agency with substantial alcohol accounts, or [with] ownership of pubs or hotels').[35]

A further thirty-nine MPs had an 'indirect interest' in alcohol (i.e. 'links through advertising, PR, newspapers' or other business connections).[36]

And before becoming Ministers – when MPs are obliged to give up their directorships and consultancies – eleven Tory MPs held direct interests in alcohol.[37] Geoffrey Finsberg, one-time junior Minister at the DHSS, was previously the parliamentary adviser to the National Union of Licensed Victuallers. Norman Fowler, who has been Secretary of State at the DHSS, was director of a subsidiary of J. Walter Thompson, one of the biggest advertising agencies in the world, with large alcohol accounts.[38]

'Fiscal legislation apart, alcohol sale and promotion is relatively free of constraints,' writes Mike Daube:

> There are few serious limitations on industry and promotion, no health warnings, easy access – with ever more outlets such as supermarkets, and all but ignored legislation on sales to minors. Governments of either complexion have been recommended firmer measures by their own advisors, but still there is little action. Even education – the last resort of the politician who wants to avoid legislation – is so low-key and ill-funded as to be almost unbelievable.[39]

And politicians have a major interest (apart from their own heavy drinking habits) in avoiding legislation: the electorate has been against it. A Sunday Times MORI poll showed in 1980 that the public was strongly opposed to large increases in the price of alcohol (74 per cent), and to a ban on advertising alcohol (70 per cent). There was also strong opposition to banning supermarket sales (63 per cent) and to tougher laws (50 per cent).

The opposition: Meanwhile, the 'sensible drinking' lobby has been comparatively badly organized. Until 1984, the four main alcohol charities were the National Council on Alcoholism (NCA), the Medical Council on Alcoholism (MCA), the Alcohol Education Centre (AEC), and the Federation of Alcoholic Rehabilitation Establishments (FARE). All of these were criticized in a 1982 DHSS/NCVO (National Council for Voluntary Organizations) report,[40] which looked at their effectiveness in reducing alcohol damage and found 'serious deficiencies'.

The MCA was criticized for having little success in helping GPs, and for failing to break resistance from medical schools to get alcoholism included in the curriculum. The AEC was criticized for running impractical and underused courses in alcohol education, and FARE was found wanting in the focus of its aims and objectives. The NCA, said the report, had failed to provide a national focus for publishing the problems of alcohol misuse, although it had done useful work in industry.

The only one of these organizations which took any serious initiative over women's drinking was FARE, which had links (through its women workers) with DAWN. When I asked Derek Rutherford, then Director of the NCA, if the NCA thought women had separate problems with alcohol, he at first said, 'No comment' – and then referred me to a female colleague: 'I would prefer you to have a woman's views,' he said, 'instead of [views] from us MCPs.'

When I asked him why there had not been a huge campaign from the NCA to alert women to the dangers of drinking in pregnancy, he reluctantly replied, 'Because of the power of vested interests. It is time [a campaign] does happen here as it has happened in the USA. This is all I dare say at this stage.'

Since the critical report was published, the main alcohol charities (excluding the MCA) have been replaced with a new national charity called Alcohol Concern set up in 1984 and funded by central government.

In 1987 Alcohol Concern published *The Drinking Revolution* which called for an investment in alcohol education, random breath testing to combat drink-driving, and for the use of alcohol taxation to reduce consumption. Alcohol Concern has proved to be a useful ally of women, according to workers in the field, and progress has been made during recent years. Alcohol Concern has also devoted a member of staff to women's concerns and has targeted money from its grant aid programme towards women.

In 1987, the Medical Royal Colleges – in the first 'consensus' between them – called for the government to give a lead in reducing the damage done by alcohol. They too wanted government action to increase alcohol taxation, to introduce random breath testing and to increase investment in alcohol education. They also called for licensing hours not to be extended.

By the end of the 1980s it seemed that the debate about alcohol was still raging over much the same ground as at the beginning of the decade. There has also been some serious losses to the anti-abuse lobby. AAA (Action on Alcohol Abuse), which had been a vocal critic of government alcohol policies, had packed up. ACCEPT, the highly successful and progressive clinic for problem drinkers, was on the verge of closure from lack of funds. In mid-1990 one ACCEPT branch was saved, five branches were taken over by local health authorities and one branch was closed. Nearly half of the hospital-based alcohol treatment units across the country had either been closed down or had their services whittled away. While in 1994, the progressive Headway Halfway House residential facility for women was closed down, a victim of the Community Care Act.

At the end of 1989, eight major drinks companies got together to set up the Portman Group with the declared aim of fighting alcohol misuse. So far, however, the Group has concentrated chiefly on trying to make drinking more socially acceptable.

John Rae, the Portman Group's Director describes the drinks industry's motives as enlightened self-interest. In a Portman Group report he writes:

> [its aims] are principally commercial. The industry knows that unless alcohol misuse can be reduced by education and by measures that target particular problems, such as drinking and driving and drink-related disorder, governments may impose across the board restrictions.

Accordingly, in 1990 the Portman Group launched a Proof of Age Card scheme to help licensees protect their licenses – and to help young people of 18 or over (but who may look younger) prove they are legally entitled to buy alcohol. It has also worked with the Department of Transport to promote anti-drink-drive campaigns; has funded research into alcohol misuse and has supported the training of teachers in alcohol education.

The Portman Group has also got media coverage for its denial that women are drinking more, together with its argument that 'lifestyle' pressures on women are having 'no effect on consumption whatsoever.'[41]

> 'The Portman Group has had an insidious effect in slanting the messages about alcohol,' says Sarah Berger, Director of DRINKLINE. 'They have effectively undermined the head of steam that was building up about alcohol problems, and the political pressure for action on alcohol abuse has declined. They scuppered the annual Drinkwise campaign in 1994 by coming out with their own report three weeks beforehand.'

There have been other problems for the anti-abuse lobby. In the latest restructuring of the Health Education Authority, 'alcohol' disappeared as a specific topic, while the annual Drinkwise day – which was for many the year's major government funded event on alcohol problems – has now been scrapped. The government's new system of Regional Alcohol Coordinators, appointed in each health region at the end of the 1980s, is also being dismantled.

If anything, alcohol problems are a lower political priority, and difficulties for those working with women in the field are worse than they were ten years ago. 'Drugs and HIV problems, as important as they are, still inspire more moral panic and attract more funds than alcohol,' says Sarah Berger. 'Drink problems remain the poor relation.'

Yet there had been some positive steps forward too with the growth of the Women's Alcohol Centre, the 1990 National Conference on alcohol services for women (organized by Alcohol Concern, DAWN and SCODA – Standing Conference On Drug Abuse), the survival and resurgence of DAWN, the range of interesting new projects set up by the Drink Crisis Centre in London and the launch of DRINKLINE – the first national telephone helpline which is used predominantly by women, many of whom are concerned about the drinking of a partner or relative. (see chapter 10 for more details).

In the meantime, our drinking, and our casualties from drinking, continue to increase. The drinks industry, at least, has counted on it: 'It is the firm view of the industry that consumption will continue to increase . . . and a number of interests in the wine trade both in this country and overseas have independently assessed the UK as a market with great potential for growth.'[42] Women also continue to misuse alcohol as more and more of us take on paid employment and the inhibitions on drinking amongst women relax.

The 1970s and early 1980s saw an 'alcoholism epidemic [which is] a public health disaster of historic proportions', according to the *British Journal of Addiction*.[43] And alcohol abuse is still one of the country's most serious and widespread health hazards although it receives far less recognition than the comparatively smaller problem of drug abuse. To combat this disaster we need educational, legislative and political changes.

We still need a major series of campaigns on the problems of alcohol, especially on the health risks to women and the dangers of drinking during pregnancy. We need regular tax increases to maintain the price of alcohol relative to the cost of living; we need a ban on alcohol advertising, a reduction in outlets, stiffer laws on drunken driving and a ban on the loosening of licensing laws.

We need better care for women with alcohol problems, and above all we need to change the social conditions which drive women to seek chemical 'solutions' to their problems and which contribute to women's lack of confidence and low self-esteem.

It is not an easy task against the massed vested interests of industry, parliament, and a government which 'is willing to trade the nation's health for profit and expedience'.[44]

Part Two

ALCOHOL AND YOUR BODY

5

BAD NEWS FOR
WOMEN DRINKERS

Alcohol affects women differently from men and its ill effects are more severe in women:

– Our bodies are generally smaller and have a higher proportion of fat to water, which means that alcohol is more concentrated in our body fluids.

– We also oxidize alcohol more slowly than men according to a 1990 report in the *New England Journal of Medicine:* in other words, we become drunk faster and remain drunk longer. This is because we have lower levels than men of the alcohol burning enzyme alcohol dehydrogenase. Researchers conclude that as a result, more alcohol enters our bloodstream and livers, and women therefore need roughly a third less alcohol than men to achieve the same level of intoxication. Women's lower levels of alcohol dehydrogenase may help explain why women are more likely to develop liver disease after drinking smaller amounts of alcohol over a shorter period of time than men.

– We are more prone to alcohol-related diseases such as liver disease than are men. And once women's livers have been damaged by alcohol, they take longer to recover than men's. We are more liable to develop digestive and nutritional problems as a consequence of drinking, and we are more likely to become dependent on alcohol.[1]

– Our response to alcohol can change during ovulation and menstruation, and we risk damage to the foetus if we drink during pregnancy.

– Millions of women in the UK are prescribed tranquillizing drugs which, in combination with alcohol, make us more vulnerable to physical and psychological damage.

– The issue of whether alcohol causes breast cancer is as yet unresolved, but an increasing number of studies are indicating a link. In 1987, a study from the *New England Journal of Medicine* showed that women who drank more than one unit of alcohol a day had a 60 per cent increased risk of breast cancer, compared with non-drinkers.

Researchers have long been saying that women should limit themselves to less than fourteen units of alcohol a week. (One unit is equivalent to half a pint of beer, a single English measure of spirits or a four fluid ounce glass of wine.) Alcohol Concern advises women to have two or three alcohol-free days each week and to avoid binge drinking. Above fourteen units you are getting into the danger zone, and women drinking over twenty-one units a week would be wise to cut down. And women who are pregnant – or planning to be – need to avoid alcohol altogether.

This is depressing news to those of us who enjoy a 'good drink', and as with all depressing news, the temptation is to forget it. It is also unwelcome for its potential as cheap-shot ammunition for arguments that we are 'weaker vessels', that women 'can't hold their drink' and so on. But to ignore the evidence of these differences is no favour to women either. It has too long been a tradition in the alcohol field that sex-related differences don't matter, and *this* is the sexist assumption. Traditionally, female alcoholism was not regarded as legitimate grounds for professional concern, and between 1929 and 1970 the topic stimulated only twenty-nine studies in the English language.[2]

Although the library shelves are groaning with learned tomes about alcohol, most of the books refer to 'alcoholics' without mentioning the sex of the subject. It is assumed that 'alcoholics' are men, and there has been a shortage of accurate information about the effects of alcohol on women.

'It is a strange fact,' said the *British Journal on Alcohol and Alcoholism* in 1982, 'that although women constitute at least half of the population, most of the information that we have about alcoholism is related to men and male rodents.'[3]

At the beginning of the 1980s I found only one British book and a handful of pamphlets and articles which were specifically about the effects of alcohol on women.[4] Almost every other publication referred to the drinker as 'he', apart from occasional references to women as exceptions from the rule. Much of the information we have about alcohol is still based on research done on men and although I have tried to fill those gaps which I became aware of and have adapted information where possible, there could be more ways not yet known to us in which alcohol affects women.

Where discoveries have been made about alcohol's effects on women – as there were in the nineteenth century and in the early 1970s about alcohol-related birth defects – these have been largely ignored, or even suppressed (see chapter 9).

There is no longer any doubt that drink can damage the foetus, but to date no British government has made this a public health issue. While American government officials have launched a campaign to warn women to avoid alcohol entirely during pregnancy (and American bars have to carry warning signs about the health risks of alcohol), the British position remains that heavy drinking during pregnancy can damage the foetus – but that alcohol is only one of many factors associated with such harm.

In 1979 the Royal College of Psychiatrists was still saying that 'heavy drinking' – i.e. 'A couple of bottles of wine taken each day – is getting into the danger area' for pregnant women. This was a ridiculous statement in view of the fact that one bottle of wine a day would be a health risk to many women, pregnant or not.

Fortunately, in the early 1980s the College revised its statement and advised pregnant women *not to drink at all.*

Then in 1987, the Royal College of Physicians in their report on the medical consequences of alcohol abuse said that 'it is probably sensible for women planning a pregnancy, or currently pregnant, to abstain from alcohol, or at least to restrict their consumption to an occasional drink, especially in the early stages of pregnancy'.[5]

But even in the 1990s, many British women are still not adequately informed of the risks. There has been no national campaign to alert women through posters or leaflets in ante-natal clinics and surgeries, although some local alcohol agencies have made an effort.

And in treatment as much as in prevention women would stand to gain a great deal from the recognition that we have separate problems and need separate attention. Despite the increases in women's alcohol problems, the services that do exist for women have been described as 'wholly inadequate'.[6] In the 1990s, there are still only a handful of residential services available for women, and only two in the country for women with children.

Blaming women

Researchers are now beginning to turn their attention to *women* and alcohol. But that is not necessarily a good thing in itself. What does matter is the *form* which this attention takes, and the ways in which new information is made public.

Some women are concerned that the interest of the male-dominated medical profession in women's alcohol problems is being expressed in unacceptable ways. Already it seems that some researchers are more interested in treating the 'interesting' female organs than in looking at *why* a woman should be putting her health at risk through drinking. The female liver becomes more important than its owner; the female's capacity to give birth deserves more care than the potential mother.

There is also the danger that the cause of alcohol abuse could become a fashionable stick for beating women, blaming them for the neglect of their families, and for the handicap of their babies. Such implications at once burden women with guilt for some-times irreversible tragedies, perpetuate the stereotype of women as irresponsible creatures (see chapter 3), and reinforce the traditional roles of women as wives and mothers with chief responsibility to the family.

A professed concern for mothers' and babies' welfare – as expressed by Right to Life campaigners (anti-abortionists) – can disguise a fundamental attack on women. The issue of the 'unborn child' is highly charged, both morally and politically, and women who have claimed the right to control their own fertility in campaigns for contraception and abortion have had bitter experience of the manipulative tactics used to oppose this demand.

Typically, emotive appeals are made in the name of the foetus, which instil guilt in women, suggest that we are unnatural and criminal if we choose not to give birth, and, by implication, reduce women to the function of 'breeders'.

We need to be on our guard against such assumptions creeping into publicity about alcohol-related birth defects. If women are going to be informed, it must not be in a tone which reflects traditional horror at the 'bad mother' (see chapter 3) and that suggests we are irresponsible and in need of constraint – if only in the interest of future generations.

And for as long as individual women are held to blame for being 'bad mothers' and/or problem drinkers, attention is diverted from the social and psychological reasons behind women's alcohol abuse. Meanwhile the profiteering of industry and government in allowing the rates of drink consumption to rise so high is forgotten, and successive governments' failures to warn women through health campaigns are ignored.

Information – or exploitation?

Where there has been debate about publicizing the issue of alcohol-related birth defects, it has been very heated. On the one hand, it is clearly important that women should be told of the risks. On the other hand, such information has to be handled with great care. Those doctors who have heard about the dangers have to consider whether anxiety and guilt in an already pregnant woman who has been drinking might be more harmful than the unquantifiable risks of alcohol.

And some feminists fear that the risks to pregnant women could too easily be exploited and sensationalized in the press. A far greater stigma is still attached to women with drink problems than to men, and the kind of publicity that reinforces this sense of shame only drives women into the vicious circle of guilty and secret drinking. Such women are even less likely to seek help before their drinking has damaged their (especially vulnerable) health.

In the course of the debate, accusations and recriminations have been hurled between researchers, campaigners and government officials. Some of those who want to publicize the issue have been called alarmists, frauds[7] or cranks by the opposition. Those who don't have been accused of everything from indifference to 'mafia' style intimidation and concealment of the facts.[8]

But information – that the causes and results of drinking in women are different from those in men – is vital if we are to make choices about our own health. At the moment, much of the existing information, and the power to make and publicize new discoveries, is in the hands of a few, mostly male, individuals. Yet as Fiona Richmond of DAWN puts it, 'the only people who really care about women are women. And women aren't represented in the research field. If we want accurate information we have to get in there and get it ourselves.'

The aim of the following chapters is to provide some of that information. Women should have early access to knowledge which could mean the difference between health and avoidable ill health – for ourselves and for our children. The manner in which we are informed is crucial, but informed we must be.

6

ABOUT ALCOHOL

What is alcohol?

Alcohol, like fire, was bound to exist. The mere storage of many products of the earth could result, under certain circumstances, in the formation of an alcoholic beverage. Alcohol, like fire, is the source of both good and evil. It can serve society meaningfully as a ritual symbol, as a means of enhancing food, as a tension releaser, as a way of developing social ease. Yet man [*sic*] has, under its influence, committed crimes of all sorts and at all levels. Alcohol, like fire, symbolizes the paradox of the human condition.[1]

Alcohol has many meanings: chemically, *alcohols* are a family of substances, but the one which we drink is C_2H_5OH, or ethyl alcohol, a colourless liquid with a sharp, burning taste. It is produced when yeast ferments the sugars in the raw materials of the drink. These sugars occur naturally in fruits and cereals such as barley, grapes and apples.

The alcohol concentration of a fermented brew can be increased tremendously when it is boiled and the vapour is collected, cooled and reliquefied. It is this process, distillation, which produces the spirits we drink.

Medically, alcohol is a depressant drug that slows the activity of the brain. Far back in history its medicinal qualities were highly valued and it was called 'the elixir of life' and reputed to have great powers of healing. It has also been used as a pain reliever (about as efficient as aspirin), and as a surgical anaesthetic (not efficient).

Alcohol is also a kind of food, containing as many calories as fat (seven per gram). It is also a disinhibiting, consciousness-altering drug, accepted in most societies as a legal, social psychotropic for adult use. In large enough quantities it is a lethal poison.

But most commonly alcohol means 'booze' – and specifically the intoxicating ingredient in alcoholic beverages. There are various ways of expressing the amount of this ingredient, but the most useful is the standard unit system. One unit of an alcoholic drink is the amount of that drink which contains approximately half an ounce of absolute alcohol. This is the amount that the liver can dispose of (oxidize) per hour in 'an average eleven-stone person'.[2] (Assuming that the 'average person' means a man, a unit of alcohol will have a greater effect on most women.) In other words, it takes about one hour to sober up for each unit of alcohol consumed.

One unit of alcohol is found in approximately half a pint of beer, a single English pub measure of spirits (⅙ gill), a glass of wine (4 fluid ounces), or a small glass (½ oz) of fortified wine (i.e. port or sherry).[3]

Another way to express the amount of intoxicating ingredient in drink is to describe the percentage of the liquid which is pure or absolute alcohol. Spirits contain approximately 40 per cent, fortified wine contains about 20 per cent, table wine about 10 per cent and beer about 5 per cent of absolute alcohol.

This system (called the European, or Gay-Lussac system) of measuring alcoholic strength, can be confused with the British 'proof spirit' system. Our system dates back to an archaic method of measuring or 'proving' the concentration of alcohol in water by adding gunpowder to the mixture. If the mixture ignited this meant that it was not less than half alcohol. Modern proof spirit is a mixture of 57 per cent spirit and 43 per cent water, so that if a spirit is described as 100 per cent proof, it contains 100 per cent of the spirit/water mixture. A bottle of gin marked 70° proof should be 70 per cent of the proof strength spirit. This is equivalent to 40 per cent (European) absolute alcohol.[4]

What happens when you drink?

Alcohol is generally swallowed and absorbed into the blood from the stomach and small intestine – although its intoxicating fumes can also be inhaled into the lungs in quite large quantities. It can also be absorbed very fast through the rectum.

The rate at which you absorb alcohol depends on several factors. If you drink on an empty stomach it will be absorbed quickly. This is why one drink before a meal often feels much more powerful than two or three afterwards. Food, especially fatty food, in the stomach will slow down the absorption process so that the alcohol concentration in the blood of a person who has just eaten will be about a quarter of the level reached in someone who has been fasting.

Bubbly drinks, such as champagne, sparkling wines, and spirits combined with a fizzy mixer will also make you drunk faster. This is because the action of the bubbles stimulates the valve which separates stomach and small intestine so that it opens wide and the alcohol passes through rapidly.

This same valve, the pylorus, will shut tightly and go into spasm if you drink too much too fast. This makes you feel sick and vomiting often follows. It is a mechanism which protects the body against larger amounts of alcohol than it can cope with.

From the gut, alcohol is absorbed into the blood and within minutes spreads throughout the body, reaching even the bones. In pregnant women, it passes into the blood of the foetus and, in women who are breastfeeding, it passes into the milk.

The blood circulation then takes it to the lungs, heart and liver. Some of it is excreted from the lungs, giving your breath the smell of alcohol. Some of it also eliminated through the kidneys and skin (which can also smell of alcohol), but the liver does about 90 per cent of the work of elimination.

If you drink at the rate of about one unit per hour, alcohol will not accumulate, but drinking faster than this or gulping drinks will end in intoxication. Whether or not you feel 'drunk' as a result will depend on the way your body 'handles' alcohol in the intricate process of absorption, distribution and elimination, and on your level of tolerance and general state of being.

And, contrary to popular belief, you cannot hurry the sobering-up process with black coffee, cold showers or fresh air. None of these will have any effect on the concentration of alcohol in your blood; they will only make you feel more awake. Sobering up is simply a matter of time.

What does alcohol do to you?

Most people are surprised to hear that alcohol is technically a 'depressant', as it has the effect of making them feel, initially at least, the opposite of depressed. But this 'lifting' effect is the result of the depressant or anaesthetizing action of alcohol on the higher centres of the brain, home of the super-ego. This is the part of the brain which controls our self-critical faculties, and when it is depressed, anxiety, caution and self-consciousness are reduced. Initially, this leaves the way clear for the feelings of confidence, relaxation and euphoria which are the goals of most drinkers.

Women and men react differently at different times to alcohol. You might have four pints one night and feel as happy as a lark – and two weeks later find yourself getting sick or in tears after drinking the same amount. But these are, in general terms, the stages of intoxication.

The first stage is 'happy'. You feel talkative, sociable and relaxed. You have fewer inhibitions and worries. There is some loss of judgement and efficiency.

The second stage is 'excited'. Your behaviour is emotional and

Diagram 1

1 = ½ pint of beer = one glass of wine = one glass of sherry = one single whisky = 20

one unit of alcohol | ½ pint of beer | one glass of wine | one glass of sherry | one single whisky | approx. 20 mgs. of blood/alcohol concentration

Diagram 2

Contains approx. **40%** alcohol — 1 bottle of spirits

Contains approx. **20%** alcohol — 1 bottle of fortified wine

Contains approx. **10%** alcohol — 1 bottle of table wine

Contains approx. **5%** alcohol — 1 pint of beer

What are the various kinds of alcoholic drinks?

erratic, your thinking is impaired and your reactions are slowed. Your judgement is poor and you lose control over some of your actions.

The third stage is 'confused'. You are staggering. You feel disoriented, moody, fearful, angry. Speech is slurred and you are seeing double.

The fourth stage is 'in a stupor'. You can't stand or walk. You are barely conscious, apathetic and inert. You are probably vomiting and incontinent.

The fifth stage is 'in a coma' and you are completely unconscious with few or no reflexes. This state may end in death from respiratory paralysis.[5]

How much alcohol?

How many drinks will take you to which stage of intoxication? Most regular drinkers can answer this question for themselves – and will know that their friends will give different answers depending on a number of factors.

For medical and legal purposes Blood Alcohol Concentration (BAC), or the number of milligrams of alcohol per millilitre of blood, is used to find out how much a person has consumed. It is important to stress, however, both that these figures can vary enormously due to a number of factors, and that alcohol is likely to have a greater effect upon women. One estimate by the Office of Health Economics (OHE) is that a pint of beer or its equivalent will give a BAC of 30 after about one hour. In an 'average person' (we can assume they mean a man) this BAC should produce a 'sense of mild well-being'. Four units of alcohol (see diagram 1) will produce a BAC of about 60 which may result in 'loss of muscular control and abnormal eye movements'.[6] Yet this is still below the British drinking and driving legal limit of 80 milligrams.

From BACs of 90 to 100 the drinker generally suffers marked impairment. From 200 to 300 most people will be semi-conscious or unconscious, and at 500 or over the drinker could well die.[7] One more practical way of remembering roughly what booze does to you is the 'Four Ds':

100mg – dizzy and delightful   200mg – drunk and disorderly
300mg – dead drunk   400mg – danger of dcath

Workers with blood levels between 30mg and 100mg have 'considerably more accidents; than those with below 30mg, according to the Health Education Council. And car drivers, they say, are more likely to have an accident after even a pint of beer (30mg). At 80mg the risk of accidents is four times greater and after about five pints (150mg), the risk is twenty-five times higher.[8]

But the snag is – and many drivers complain about it – that we have no simple way of predicting how drunk one person will get after how much drink. Regular drinkers are inclined to scoff at these estimates of how much booze makes them incapable as bearing no relation to how they feel after four pints on a Friday evening. And it is true that 'rates' of getting drunk and sobering up can only be estimated, as individuals and their levels of tolerance vary so greatly. And again, most of the work on assessing these rates refers to the drinker as 'he'.

How much drink you can 'hold' depends on how much you are used to. It is also affected by your state of mind and general health, and by how much food you have eaten and how recently. Your body weight and stage of menstrual cycle will also make for differences.

And, as I've said, alcohol *does* affect men and women differently. Very little alcohol enters fatty tissue, as this tissue has a poor blood supply, and women have a higher proportion of fat to water than men. Young women have about 50 per cent of their total body weight in the form of water, as opposed to 60 per cent for young men. This means that even if a woman is the same weight as a man, she is going to get drunk faster as the pool of liquid in which her drink is diffused is smaller – and so the concentration of alcohol will be higher. Also, most women are smaller than men to start with, so that alcohol's effects are even more concentrated, and we have lower levels of the alcohol burning enzyme, alcohol dehydrogenase. This means we get drunk faster and stay drunk longer.

Tolerance

Perhaps the most important factor to affect how 'drunk' you get is your level of tolerance to alcohol. Most of us can remember getting giggly or silly or weepy on just a couple of drinks when we first took alcohol, and many beginner drinkers get sick and giddy as well.

But although this response shows itself in physical discomforts, it is actually the brain's reaction to a rush of unfamiliar sensations. People who smoke marijuana for the first time often feel sick for the same reasons, in reaction to the alteration in their consciousness.

After more experience with drink (as with drugs) most people are better able to cope with it, and in larger quantities. This change shows that they are developing psychological or behavioural tolerance to drink. Some heavy drinkers eventually 'learn' to cope with huge amounts of alcohol without seeming to be drunk – a dangerous situation for their health. It also happens that after a high degree of tolerance has been maintained for years in heavy drinkers the process may go into reverse, and she or he starts getting drunk very quickly on small amounts.

This process of developing tolerance has been compared to that of a child ('he' again . . .) growing up:

> Just as a newborn baby, unable at first to coordinate any of his movements, learns eventually to grasp with his hands, then stand up, then walk, and talk, then operate computers or space vehicles, so the drunk, given sufficient experience, can learn to cope with his state. In his vaudeville days for instance, W. C. Fields was able to perform six acts daily of intricate jugglery while on a one-to-two-quarts-of-gin-per-day drinking regime. Fields had 'learned' the drunken state and could function within it.[9]

In addition to this behavioural tolerance which most 'social' drinkers soon develop, the body has the capacity to develop a higher level of physical tolerance to alcohol. Very heavy drinkers can 'learn' to metabolize alcohol more quickly than usual, and surgeons have found that alcoholic patients require larger doses of anaesthetics than non-drinkers. This is because, together with physical tolerance to alcohol, very heavy drinkers may show a cross-resistance to substances like ether and chloroform.[10]

On one level, then, learning how to handle drink is valued as a social skill which stops most of us making fools of ourselves in pubs or at parties. But on another level developing tolerance is a dangerously insidious process, which allows us to pass for sober when we are not. It is a process which is linked to the so-called 'alcohol-dependence syndrome' or 'alcoholism' (see chapter 10) in which many drinkers get well out of their depth – before they realize the danger.

Timing

The timing of your drinking will also affect how drunk you feel – and how you feel when drunk – independently of blood alcohol levels.

By eleven o'clock at night, after a few pleasant pints in the pub, you will most likely be in a mellow mood, confident and relaxed. Your blood alcohol level is probably about 80mg. You are on the 'up-curve' of drinking and enjoying the (subjectively) stimulating effects of alcohol.

But although drink makes you *feel* more capable by removing your anxieties, it actually stops you from functioning as well as you do when sober – unless you are an exceptionally nervous character. Alcohol has a negative effect on concentration, memory, judgement and insight, and limits your attention span and reaction time – all good reasons not to drive at this level of drinking.

Not all of the parts of your brain are affected to the same extent, or the same amounts of drink which make you 'drunk' would at the same time affect systems like your breathing mechanism. It is the most sophisticated processes of thought and coordination which are clouded at first, so that your movements become clumsy and your thinking erratic.

Had you left the pub in this mellow state at eleven o'clock and gone to a party where you had more drinks, your confidence might have grown into euphoria. You would have felt able for anything, capable of saying anything to anyone. This is the drinking 'up-curve'.

Yet the next morning, while going through the painful process of sobering up, your blood alcohol level would again pass the 80mg point – on the way down. In contrast to the same point the night before when your level was 80mg, you are likely to feel clumsy, inept and probably anxious and guilty. You are on the drinking 'down-curve' and you are feeling the depressant and toxic effects of alcohol.

Drinkers do commonly judge themselves to be less inept while getting drunk than when hungover, but tests on memory, attention and coordination have shown that the reverse is true. Both

What happens if you have been drinking at lunchtime and then drink again in the late afternoon

Diagram 3

100 mg
90
80 — — — — Legal limit — — — — — — — — —
70
60 — — — Driving increasingly affected — — —
50
40   Increased likelihood
30 — — — of accidents — — — — — — — —
20
10

0   1   2   3   4   5   6   7   8   9   10   11   12   TIME

1 glass of sherry, 2 glasses of wine   2 pints of beer   MIDNIGHT
1 brandy at lunchtime   after work

men and women score *less* in these categories on the up-curve than they do on the down-curve, but, on the up-curve women score less than men in motor coordination, and more than men on attention. Driving requires both of these skills – which means that one sex is no safer than the other in taking the car home from the party.

And on the morning after – or any morning – you are unlikely to want a stiff drink as soon as you wake up (unless you have problems of dependence and withdrawal). By the evening, however, 'when the sun is over the yard-arm' – a pint of beer is a much more tempting prospect.

It has been suggested that we have some sort of biological clock which dictates the timing of healthy drinking habits – from which follow traditional pub opening hours and social conventions about when you should drink. In a rather objectionable experiment with mice, 60 per cent of the animals reportedly died when dosed with vodka at their time of awakening, while the same dose given to the mice as a 'nightcap' killed 12 per cent of them.

One somewhat romantic conclusion is that 'the person who waits until sundown to start drinking is more in tune with the tides of life than the one who starts first thing in the morning'.[11] Whether this is true or not, the person who waits until sundown is certainly less likely to develop alcohol problems.

Drinking twice a day: Because your system can only metabolize so much alcohol in a given time, drinking twice a day or topping up throughout the day will have a cumulative effect.

Men, more than women, are in (better) paid jobs and follow a pattern of going to the pub at lunch hour and again after work. The following explanation, based on a Health Education Council leaflet, assumes this male pattern (its illustrations show men), but it does apply with equal or greater force to women who drink twice a day.

If you have a boozy lunch which includes, say, a sherry, two glasses of wine and a liqueur, and then pop down to the pub when it opens after work for a couple of pints of lager, you are likely to get a lot drunker than you bargained for.

The lunchtime drink would raise your blood alcohol level to about 85mg. This will sink gradually throughout the afternoon, but at 5.30 p.m. will still be above the sober level. After two evening pints, however, your blood alcohol level will be back above the legal driving limit – at about 90mg. Not only can you lose your licence at this stage but you are four times more likely to have an accident than when sober (see diagram 3).

The same banking-up effect can affect your morning-after. If you were to go to bed at one a.m. after four glasses of wine and a double brandy – or six pints of beer – your blood alcohol level would be about 200mg.

The alcohol in your blood would still be above the legal driving limit at 8.00 a.m., and you would be more likely to have an accident at work until mid-morning (see diagram 4).

7

ALCOHOL IN YOUR BODY

The menstrual cycle

Your reaction to alcohol is also likely to vary according to the stages of your menstrual cycle. Many women find that just a couple of drinks – which might ordinarily have a mildly mellowing effect – will make them feel quite unexpectedly drunk while they are ovulating or premenstrual. (It is worth bearing this in mind if you are driving.)

For a few days before menstruating and at ovulation, the concentration of alcohol in the blood is higher – and it stays there for longer.

As a result of these fluctuations, women have a less predictable response to drink than men do. Women on the Pill will have a more regular response, but they will metabolize alcohol more slowly and so stay drunk longer.

And many women drink for relief from premenstrual tension, post-natal depression, and from depression around the time of the menopause. Alcohol, with its cheering, relaxing effect, *seems* like the ideal balm for these problems. But for some women, the long-term consequences of the 'cheering drink' can be severe.

Judy Lever, in her book on premenstrual tension, writes that 'since alcohol in the long term is a depressant, anxiety-producing, addictive drug, you may find over-drinking becoming a regular monthly routine, and the slide into alcoholism begins'.[1]

It is common for women to drink more before their periods in the hope of curing the premenstrual 'blues'. In an American survey, 67 per cent of women alcoholics related their drinking bouts to their menstrual cycle and all of them said that their drinking had begun or increased during the premenstrual period.[2]

Alcoholic clinics have also found that women drink more heavily in the week before their period and are inclined to relapse – if they have been trying to stay 'dry' – in this week. Charles Vetter of ACCEPT identifies the 'vulnerability period' as ten days or so before menstruation. He says that during this time the extra strain of PMT can sap women's will-power and make them feel miserable. A likely response is for a woman to start drinking again to cheer herself up.

Vetter has asked women to keep a diary of their drinking habits and periods and has consistently found that women who have been coping well, will start to feel desperate before their period and will turn to alcohol. One of ACCEPT's women clients had seven relapses into drinking – and her diary showed that all of them coincided with the three or four days before her period.

Sexuality

Alcohol affects our moods, initially making us more confident, relaxed and outgoing. It follows that drinking may make some women feel less inhibited too, so that we end up having – perhaps unexpected – sexual encounters. Geraldine Nolan of DAWN cites a Swedish study which showed that 80 per cent of adolescents had their first sexual experience under the influence of alcohol.

And according to new research into the effects of alcohol on the sex drives of men and women,[3] relatively small amounts of alcohol can cause a dramatic but temporary surge of the male sex hormone testosterone in women, increasing sexual desire. The effect is strongest in women taking the Pill who have low levels of testosterone to begin with.

The guilt which women tend to suffer after drinking may be

compounded by guilt about having sex. And because unexpected sex is often unprotected sex (particularly for younger women) there is the risk of unwanted pregnancy and the increased possibility of contracting sexually transmitted diseases, including HIV/AIDS.

Several studies have shown that drinking alcohol is linked with 'risky' sex, in particular the failure to use condoms. A survey of young women who had married in their teens showed that of those who had been drinking when they first had sex, only 13 per cent used condoms. By contrast, 57 per cent of young women who had not been drinking when they lost their virginity did use condoms.

Another study of the drinking habits of young people has shown that men and women who regularly combine drinking and sex are seven times less likely than others to use condoms.[4]

The digestive system: eat, drink and be merry

As far as your digestive system is concerned, alcohol – like much else that we swallow – is beneficial in moderation and damaging in excess. This is not the place for a gourmet guide to drink: suffice to say that alcohol can be a delicious accompaniment to food as an aperitif, an ingredient, and as a complement to a meal. And it can be delicious in itself.

But as a type of food, alcohol's value is very limited. It gives as many calories as fat (seven calories per gram) and alcoholics are said to literally 'run on spirit'.

These are 'empty' calories, however, with few of the minerals, proteins or vitamins which are essential to nutrition. When alcohol is substituted for food – as it often is in 'liquid lunches' or 'binges' – the body is deprived of essential nutrients.

Alcohol also interferes with the body's ability to use other sources of energy. Alcoholics often neglect to eat and it has been said that alcoholism is the major cause of malnutrition in the western world.

And all drinkers know that alcohol makes you urinate a lot. This is not simply a result of taking in all that extra liquid; it happens because one of the hormones which controls the amount of urine your body produces is affected by drink. When you have alcohol in your body, too little of this hormone is produced, and so too much urine results.

Getting fat

Drinking can make you fat – unless you balance your intake of food and alcohol properly, and take exercise. The number of calories that your body burns depends on various factors such as your metabolism, your size and how physically active you are. But very roughly women need about 2,000 calories a day to stay at the same weight (as opposed to 2,500 to 3,000 for men).

Alcohol is full of calories. A pint of beer has about 180 calories, a pub measure of whisky has about 50 and a glass of wine has about 80-100 (see table on page 119).

This means that by drinking five pints of beer in the course of a day, you are taking in about *half* of your daily calorie requirement. If you continue eating normally (i.e. at 2,000 calories a day), which you need to do to maintain the level of essential nutrients present in food but not in alcohol, you will probably gain weight. It has been estimated that alcoholic beverages now account for approximately one-twentieth of the nation's calorie intake.

It takes about 3,000 calories to add a pound of fat to the body, so if you continue eating normally and drinking five pints a day you could put on about a pound a week.

The best way to cope with these extra calories is simply to drink less. But if you won't or can't do that, extra exercise will help to burn them up.

Taking alcohol before and with meals has long been considered a 'civilized' custom in many cultures – and with good reason. Apart from the social and psychological advantages of having a drink at mealtimes, there is a physical bonus in that moderate

Diagram 5

Aggressive, irrational behaviour.
Arguments. Violence. Depression.
Nervousness. Chronic anxiety.
Unknown fears. Hallucinations.
Serious psychiatric disorders.
Epilepsy. Dementia (wet brain).

Blackouts (alcohol amnesia)
Serious memory loss.
Damage to nerves.

Facial deterioration.
Puffy eyes. 'Drinker's
Nose'. Looking older.

Chronic coughing. Throat cancer
(cancer of the larynx.)

Weakness of heart muscle.
Heart failure.
Anaemia, impaired
blood clotting.
High blood pressure.

Cancer of the oesophagus.

Frequent colds.
Reduced resistance to
infection. Increased
risk of pneumonia
and tuberculosis.

Breast cancer.

Vitamin deficiency.
Haemorrhage. Severe
inflammation of the
stomach. Vomiting.
Diarrhoea. Malnutrition.

Inflammation of
the pancreas.

Impaired kidney function.
Urinary infections.

Trembling hands.
Tingling fingers.
Numbness, loss of
sensation in the fingers.
Peripheral neuritis.

Liver damage leading
to breakdown and
cirrhosis and liver cancer.

Duodenal ulcer.

Unwanted pregnancies, risk
of giving birth to deformed,
retarded babies, or low
birth weight babies. Risk
of contracting HIV/AIDS
after unprotected sex.

Impaired sensation leading to
falls and numbness causing
skin damage.

Numb, tingling toes.
Peripheral neuritis.

**WHERE ALCOHOL
MISUSE TAKES
ITS TOLL**

amounts of drink aid digestion, hence the practice of taking an aperitif and of drinking wine with meals. A few drinks stimulate the flow of saliva and gastric acid in the stomach. These juices are necessary for digestion, but people with peptic ulcers should avoid alcohol as the extra acidity causes discomfort.

And too much alcohol has an adverse effect, delaying the absorption of food and causing vomiting. High concentrations of alcohol will also irritate the stomach lining, causing inflammation and erosions. About a third of heavy drinkers have chronic stomach problems, such as gastritis. The duodenum (beginning of the small intestine) and the oesophagus (tube leading from the mouth to the stomach) are also badly affected by too much drink. Women drinkers are especially prone to stomach and duodenal ulcers, nutritional problems and anaemia. Cancer of the oesophagus is also more common in alcoholics than in the rest of the population, and heavy smoking has a 'synergic' (working together) effect, multiplying the risk of cancer already increased by drinking.[5]

Your liver

The liver has many intricate and important functions. It is the largest gland in the body. It fuels us (by maintaining our level of blood sugar, the only form of energy the brain can use). It purifies our blood (by removing toxins and impurities). It breaks down proteins and stores fats and vitamins. It also handles the chemical breakdown of alcohol – and in the process, because of differences in our metabolism and immune system, women are far more vulnerable to damage than men.

The liver metabolizes (changes chemically) all but 10 per cent of the alcohol we drink. The first step is to change alcohol to acetaldehyde, a task done by liver enzymes. Then acetaldehyde is changed to acetic acid which leaves the liver, is dispersed through the body and broken down by other organs.

But when the liver has large amounts of alcohol to deal with it 'forgets' some of its other functions. Most of us who have had hangovers have experienced the unpleasant symptoms of nervousness, sweating, headache and trembling. This is because alcohol is not available to the body as sugar – despite the fact that it is made from sugar and high in calories – and furthermore, it interferes with the body's efforts to maintain a proper blood sugar level.

These hangover symptoms, together with hunger and weakness, are signs that the liver is failing to maintain normal blood sugar levels. Drinking on an empty stomach, or drinking so much with a meal that alcohol is still around after the food is digested, can bring on this state, known as hypoglycaemia. (It also partly accounts for the 'drinkers' munchies', that recurring desire for chips on the way home from the pub or chocolate biscuits the morning after.) Hypoglycaemia, if the body's blood sugar levels drop low enough, results in coma.

And the liver develops its own problems when repeatedly subjected to doses of alcohol. Normally, it 'burns' fat. But as soon as alcohol reaches the liver, it stops doing this and the fat content of the liver rises. The end result is a condition called 'fatty liver' which may cause other complications. Not just heavy drinkers, but moderate drinkers can develop fatty liver.

For as long as the liver is healthy it occupies a place just below the ribs in the upper right abdomen. If it becomes diseased, however, it can swell up and protrude from beneath the ribs.

For reasons connected with our immune system and metabolism, women are far more prone to liver disease – and in its severe and fatal forms – than men. Dr Roger Williams of King's College Hospital has found that of his patients in the Liver Unit it is the women who suffer more often and have more severe liver damage from alcohol. He also finds that women are particularly likely to develop a form of inflammation of the liver known as alcoholic hepatitis.

The symptoms of this are fever, a high white blood-cell count, pain in the upper right abdomen and jaundice. It usually subsides

Calories in alcoholic drinks:

Beers: per pint

Bitter	180
Brown Ale	170
Stout	200
Light ale	150
Mild ale	150
Pale ale	180
Most home-brewed beers	240
Pils (per bottle)	105

Ciders: per half pint

Dry	100
Sweet	120
Babycham	78

Lagers: per pint 160-180

Stella Artois	240
Special strength lager (half-pint bottle)	205
Non-alcoholic lager (275 ml can)	45-55

Sherry: ($1/3$ gill)

Dry	55
Medium	60
Cream	65

Port: ($1/3$ gill)   75

Spirits: (pub measure: $1/6$ gill)

Brandy	75
Whisky	58
Rum	75
Gin	55
Vodka	63

Wines: (per glass)

Dry white	75
Sweet white	100
Rosé	80
Dry red	80
Sweet red	95
Champagne	90-110
Non-alcoholic wine	30

Aperitifs: (pub measure: $1/3$ gill)

Martini, dry	84
Martini, sweet	98
Ouzo	60
Pernod	65
Campari	111

Liqueurs: (pub measure: $1/6$ gill)

Benedictine	90
Cointreau or Drambuie	85
Crème de Menthe	80
Grand Marnier	80
Bailey's Irish Cream	85

Mixers:

Fruit juices (bottles)

Grapefruit	65
Orange	60
Tomato	25
Soda water or mineral water	0
Bitter lemon (4 fl oz)	40
Tonic water (4 fl oz)	25-40
Lime juice cordial (1 fl oz)	25
Dry ginger ale (4 fl oz)	15
Lemonade (4 fl oz)	30
Cola	80

when the patient stops drinking, but Dr Williams has found that in women, hepatitis is more likely to develop into cirrhosis and to end in early death. This is particularly true for women below forty-five years of age, or before the age of menopause. But if and how the menopause affects women's livers is not yet understood.

When liver damage becomes so severe that scarring occurs (and this can happen for reasons besides drinking, such as infection), the liver ceases to function properly and cirrhosis develops. The liver fails in its task of removing impurities from the blood, the abdominal cavity may fill with fluid (dropsy) and the arms and legs become spindly. In men, the testes atrophy and breasts enlarge, while women stop menstruating and their breasts either enlarge or, more usually, shrink. If the disease is caught in time, these symptoms can be reversed, but if the drinker continues to take alcohol, cirrhosis can lead to death.

Cirrhosis was, until recently, generally considered to be a disease of elderly or middle-aged, heavily drinking men. But the number of women admitted to UK hospitals with the disease has increased about four-fold in the last decade and some 40 per cent of cirrhosis patients are now women.

Dr John Saunders, also of King's College Hospital Liver Unit, thinks women should be warned about the risks they take with alcohol at even low levels of drinking: 'Women may develop cirrhosis if their daily intake exceeds 40 grams of alcohol.' This is the equivalent of about two and a half pints of beer, four glasses of wine or two double measures of spirits – yet these are amounts that many women consider quite socially acceptable. (Men are not at risk until their daily intake exceeds 80 grams, according to Dr Saunders.)

Cirrhosis also develops more rapidly in women than in men: it takes on average thirteen years of excessive drinking for a woman to develop symptoms of cirrhosis, compared with twenty-two for a man.

Dr Sheila Sherlock, of the Royal Free Hospital School of Medicine, puts the 'safe limit' for women even lower – at half the levels suggested by Dr Saunders. She estimates that 'as little as 20 grams of alcohol daily (about one and a half pints of beer, half a bottle of wine or two and a half measures of spirits) exposes the drinkers to serious liver damage'. This, however, is her lowest 'safe' estimate and she sets a 'more realistic' average level of risk at 60 grams in women – as compared to about 80 for men.[6]

Fortunately, the liver does have an extraordinary capacity to function as required, even when up to two-thirds of its cells have been destroyed. It also has the power to replace its own damaged cells over a period of time. This is why 'binge' drinking seems to be less harmful to the liver than regular drinking, as the liver regenerates itself given a few 'days off'.

And not everyone who drinks excessively develops liver damage. The experts still don't know why but, according to Dr Sherlock, numerous 'chronic alcoholics [have] completely normal livers'.

Your heart and blood stream

It is a popular – but false – notion that a good belt of alcohol will warm you up'. Pubs sell 'winter warmers' when the weather turns cold, and we are all familiar with the image of the friendly St Bernard dog, bringing sustenance in the form of brandy to freezing victims in the snow.

But although alcohol will make you feel warm temporarily by sending blood rushing to the skin capillaries, the end result is loss of blood heat through the skin and so a lowering of temperature.

Alcohol increases blood flow to the brain, but in moderate amounts has only minor effects on heartbeat and blood pressure in most people. Angina sufferers do say, however, that a few drinks reduce the pain in their hearts, but this is probably the result of depression of the pain centres in the brain rather than of improved flow of blood to the heart.

In people suffering from ischaemic heart disease (lack of blood to the heart muscle) – which kills one-quarter of the UK population – moderate amounts of alcohol can produce arrhythmia, or lack of rhythm in the heart, which can lead to death. High blood pressure too could be caused primarily by alcohol in 10 to 30 per cent of cases.[7]

Chronic drinking over many years will produce changes in the heart just as it does in the liver and nervous system. Because it is a poison, alcohol taken in large enough quantities kills the cells of the heart, causing a condition called cardiomyopathy. The heart dilates and grows massive in the attempt to replace the dead cells, but stops functioning efficiently. Heart failure and death can result.

On the positive side, there is some evidence that alcohol can prevent coronary disease, which is less common in the wine-drinking countries than elsewhere.

As for the popular idea that a few drinks a day will help you relax and so keep heart trouble away, Dr Butler, of the British Heart Foundation, says this is 'splitting hairs' . . . 'There are so many factors involved in heart attacks that it is rubbish to say that a couple of gins a day are going to protect you.'

From another point of view, this could suggest that you might as well relax and enjoy a few drinks now and then . . .

Alcohol and other drugs

Not only is women's drinking on the increase, but women's use of psychotropic drugs (drugs that affect the psyche, or conscious and unconscious mind – such as tranquillizers) has shot up in recent years. Estimates do vary, but women consume about twice as many psychotropic drugs as men. And because alcohol is a drug itself, its effects, when mixed with other drugs, can be particularly dangerous.

Alcohol has a similar 'depressant' effect on your central nervous system to many other drugs, and so in combination the two can 'add' or 'multiply' each other's effects. It is worth asking your doctor and your chemist if you can safely drink while taking the drugs they dispense to you. (If you are appalled at the prospect of stopping drinking while a course of pills lasts, it is time for you to take a long hard look at your drinking habits: according to some definitions (see chapter 10) you have a 'problem'.)

Below are some of the more common drugs which, taken with alcohol, will 'add' to each other's depressant effects – with results varying from drowsiness, loss of coordination, to coma death:

Analgesics: these are painkillers like aspirin and
  paracetamol
Anti-histamines: these are drugs used against allergies, i.e
  Phenergan, Piriton
Sedatives and tranquillizers: i.e. Valium, Librium and
  Largactil
Hypnotics: sleeping pills, such as Mogadon and barbiturates
Anti-convulsants: these are prescribed to control fits,
  mainly epileptic, i.e. barbiturates, Phenytoin

When alcohol is mixed with barbiturates (such as Tuinal Nembutal) the effect can be especially dangerous and even lethal, as the two drugs multiply ('potentiate') each other's effect. The result of combining the two is therefore greater than the sum of the two doses.

When mixed with amphetamines, which are stimulants, alcohol can cause you to become excited or agitated and to behave in an unpredictable fashion.

If you take anti-depressants and drink, your coordination and concentration can suffer. And even a small amount of alcohol slows down the metabolism of other drugs so that they stay in your system longer.

Some drugs such as antibiotics (which stop the spread of infection, i.e. penicillin, tetracyclines) and anti-coagulants (these thin the blood and are used for heart trouble, i.e. warfarin, heparin), will be less effective in their therapeutic role if you drink while taking them. Alcohol with some antibiotics reduces the amount of vitamins in the body, while drinking with some antibiotics (such as Flagyl) can make you very sick.

Nor is it a good idea to mix drink with aspirin. Both of these drugs irritate the stomach lining and, if taken together, can cause bleeding in the stomach and difficulty in blood clotting. And don't take paracetamol with alcohol: you could seriously damage your liver.

8

ALCOHOL AND PREGNANCY

Drinking alcohol during pregnancy can damage the foetus and cause babies to be born with a range of mental and physical defects. The most severe combination of these which sometimes occurs in children is called Foetal Alcohol Syndrome or FAS.

However, motherhood and alcohol are highly emotive issues and the whole subject of drinking during pregnancy calls for a common-sense approach. We now know that alcohol goes from a woman's blood into the foetus and therefore it makes sense to avoid alcohol in pregnancy.

Yet it also makes sense to avoid working too hard, smoking cigarettes, breathing polluted air, eating poor quality food and being young, poor and generally unsupported in pregnancy. But we don't hear of problems called Foetal Poverty Syndrome, or Foetal Tobacco Syndrome – or hear of anxious industrialists and politicians fretting guiltily over the damage they may have done to the unborn.

Much of the research which suggests that even small quantities of alcohol can damage a foetus comes from America, a country with a strong puritan tradition. In Britain, however, the latest research round-up, published by the Royal College of General Practitioners,[1] found that foetal harm was 'associated with several factors: e.g., the mother's previous obstetric history, socio-economic status, tobacco smoking, height, diet, use of prescribed and illicit drugs, age and marital status . . . Alcohol per se is only one of a constellation of factors associated with such harm'.

This study concluded that women who had consumed ten units or more at one time in the first three months of pregnancy were 'significantly more likely than other women to produce babies with abnormalities.' Yet, the Royal College report emphasises, 'moderate (i.e. up to 5 units a week) alcohol intake during pregnancy did not appear to cause any damage to the developing foetus.'

Warnings from the past

Taboos against drinking by would-be mothers and fathers date back to Old Testament times. 'You are barren and have no child, but you shall conceive and give birth to a son,' says the Angel of the Lord to a childless woman in the Book of Judges (13.7). 'Now you must do as I say: be careful to drink no wine or strong drink.'

In Carthage, bridal couples were banned from drinking on their wedding night in case they should conceive in a state of drunkenness and give birth to deformed children.[2]

And Aristotle, never renowned for his high opinion of women, wrote that 'foolish, drunken or harebrain women for the most part bring forth children like unto themselves, morosos et languidos'.

In Britain, evidence of FAS was produced centuries ago: when James Sedgewick wrote *A New Treatise on Liquors* in 1725 he echoed Aristotle's tone in blaming women for the results of their drinking: 'Half of the train of chronical diseases with which we see children afflicted are only the secondary sighs and groanings, the evident marks and reproaches of parental ill-spent life . . . These consequences may, nay without doubt will, be brought on infants, by the debauchery of the mother.' His conclusion was that women must be brought under control: 'The regulation of the mother during her pregnancy is an affair of the highest moment and consideration.'

The House of Commons heard evidence about alcohol's effects

on the unborn as far back as 1834, when a select committee was told that babies of heavy-drinking mothers tended to be born 'starved, shrivelled and imperfect in form'.[3]

Then in 1899, William Sullivan, a doctor to a Liverpool prison, reported the first case study of women who drank heavily in pregnancy. He found that the women 'drunkards' in the jail had an infant mortality and stillbirth rate of 56 per cent – more than twice as high as that among their non-alcoholic female relatives.

He also found that some of the alcoholic women who had previously given birth to severe or even fatally damaged babies later gave birth to healthy children after being imprisoned – without drink – during pregnancy. Sullivan's conclusion was that 'maternal intoxication' was the chief source of damage to the foetus in these cases.[4]

The present picture

Only during the 1970s and 1980s was information drawn together to pinpoint the syndrome which we now know as FAS. Most of the work has been done in America and Europe and the French and the Americans have launched major public health campaigns to warn pregnant women about drinking. British women, however, are still more likely to have the attitude that 'a few drinks won't hurt'.

Early reports of the FAS phenomenon came from France in 1968 where researchers described 127 children of alcoholic women who had remarkably similar facial features and growth deficiencies.[5]

Five years later, *The Lancet* published American research which showed that similar patterns of malformation in eight unrelated children born to alcoholic mothers had been found.[6] The children had similar facial features, growth deficiencies and mental retardation.

This report sparked off international interest, and in the following years, hundreds of case reports were published.

Throughout the seventies more evidence emerged that alcohol could cause a broad spectrum of damage to the foetus. Dr Ann Streissguth, who directed a study into FAS at the University of Washington School of Medicine, lists these as the chief risks to the foetus:[7]

- mental retardation
- retarded growth
- central nervous system abnormalities
- a variety of malformations
- death of the foetus within the uterus

Babies born with FAS symptoms may have the same problems of withdrawal from alcohol as adults, experiencing tremors, irritability, spontaneous seizures and increased respiration rate.

Identifying Foetal Alcohol Syndrome

Much of the controversy over FAS stems from the difficulties in recognizing it. The features of the syndrome are *not* unique and can vary greatly in their severity. Malnutrition, smoking and other drugs may have similar effects to alcohol on the foetus. Because of this overlap, many doctors have thought that FAS symptoms were the result of Down's syndrome or some of the other disorders which share the FAS features.

But the accumulating evidence shows that when the full pattern of FAS is present, alcohol is always there in the mother's history. FAS has been recognized in babies *before* it was known that their mothers were alcoholic, whereas it has not been found in cultures where alcohol is not abused – even when the diet is very poor.[8]

And until we make a concerted effort to ensure that more women and doctors are aware of FAS, it will continue to go unrecognized – and unprevented.

Symptoms of FAS: FAS babies are typically underweight and small in body-length when born. They don't grow or develop well, and if seriously affected will not catch up mentally or physically with other babies. The mother – especially if she is drinking – may be blamed for the neglect of the child, continues to look thin and ill. But even when hospitalized or taken into care the baby fares no better.[9]

Towards adolescence the child may put on more weight, but his or her IQ doesn't necessarily improve with age. FAS babies are generally mentally disabled with IQs ranging from 16 to 105, with a (mean) average of 65 (the national average is 100). As a baby he or she is often fractious, tremulous and has a feeble sucking response, and in childhood is likely to be hyperactive and a slow developer.

The 'cluster' of facial features which indicate FAS include a small head; shortened eyeslits; an underdeveloped upper lip; a short, snub nose; flattened profile and small chin. The eyelids may also be drooping and the eyes crossed.

Some of the vital organs can also be affected. Heart defects are common (about 30 per cent) in FAS babies, who may also have abnormal kidneys, slightly malformed genitals and abnormalities of the joints and palmar creases.[10]

It is important to stress that one by one these features may be hardly noticeable and may have nothing at all to do with FAS. Some of them occur for other reasons in babies of women who have never touched alcohol. But together these features form a characteristic 'constellation' which suggests FAS.

How else does alcohol affect pregnancy and childbirth?

Even small amounts of alcohol may increase the risk of decreased birth weight, stillbirth and spontaneous abortion. Some research has suggested that the risk of spontaneous abortion increases amongst women who drink two units or more twice a week. Women who drink between seven and fourteen units a week in the first three months of pregnancy are twice as likely to miscarry. Why some pregnancies are affected – but not others – is still not understood.[11] And in an American study (reported by *Alcohol Concern* magazine, June 1989, from the *International Herald Tribune*), even women who drank alcohol moderately in the first month or two of pregnancy, often before they realized they were pregnant, had children who showed some impairment of intellectual development.

Dr Ann Streissguth has recommended that women who are trying to become pregnant – or who might become so – should not drink alcohol at all. She believes the effects on children occur even at the social-drinking level and that babies of 'social drinkers' can suffer from tremors and may not sleep well – even when they show no FAS symptoms.

Dr Streissguth has said that even an average of two drinks a day during pregnancy could nearly double the chances that a baby will be stillborn, be smaller than normal, or will suffer from some other congenital defect.[12] And babies who are born with a low birth weight are prone to early health problems and vulnerable to infection.

However, recent research into babies' birth weight (from Professor Ross Anderson and colleagues at St George's Hospital in London, reported by Alcohol Concern in June 1989 from the *British Medical Journal*, Vol. 298, pages 795-800) showed that alcohol does have a measurable effect on the birth weight of babies, but only on the babies of women who smoked as well as drank. Cigarette smoking was judged to be the only universal factor to influence low birth weight in babies.

Drinking alcohol at the time of childbirth and during breast-feeding can also be harmful to the child. Women sometimes take alcohol to relieve the pain of labour or to hold back premature labour. But the alcohol will pass into the baby's blood, adversely affecting its breathing, central nervous system and bone cells.

Many nursing mothers used to be advised by doctors that having a drink would help them to relax. Yet not only does alcohol appear in the breast milk, but the process of ejecting it from the breast can be slowed down by alcohol.[13] On the other hand, mothers of young children are often under enormous stress and may well decide that if having a drink helps them cope, this is the lesser of two evils.

American researchers have also found a relationship between 'alcoholism' and a high incidence of gynaecological and obstetric problems such as infertility, miscarriages and hysterectomy.[14] But which of these problems comes first, or causes the other, is not yet understood.

Very little research has been done into the effects of alcohol on male sperm and its possible consequent effect on the foetus. But it is known that drink is a testicular toxin and heavy drinking in men (five or more drinks a day) can result in reduced production of sperm and production of abnormal sperm. According to Dr Richard Smith, a member of the Royal College of Physicians' working party on alcohol,[15] 'almost half of the men attending an infertility clinic had sperm damaged by alcohol, and on average they drank two to three pints of beer a day'.

How does alcohol damage the foetus?

Until about the 1940s, scientists thought that the uterus was virtually unaffected by harmful substances in the mother's body – but in the early sixties the thalidomide tragedy changed those ideas once and for all. And now alcohol has joined the long list of 'environmental' agents with the potential to damage the foetus.

No one yet knows exactly how FAS, or other alcohol-related birth defects, are caused. It is not known *when* or in what *quantity* drink will affect the foetus. Researchers are still trying to discover why some babies and not others are affected: twins have been born, one with and one without FAS symptoms.

Nor do we know whether the mechanisms of FAS work exclusively through the mother, or whether the father's drinking can result in a malformed foetus if the father's sperm is affected by alcohol at the time of conception.

Safe limits: is it true that 'a few drinks won't hurt'?

In Britain, the Royal College of Psychiatrists has said that 'even very moderate social drinking may be associated with decreased birth weight and increased risk of spontaneous abortion.'[16]

Although it is difficult to put a figure on exactly how many drinks may be dangerous, say the College, 'the woman who is drinking "alcoholically" is certainly putting her baby at risk, but it is possible that lesser degrees of deformity may occur even with more moderate drinking'.

Their conclusion is clear: 'Pregnant women would be well advised not to drink alcohol during pregnancy.'

American health officials have been saying so – and much more emphatically – for years. 'For baby's sake and yours, don't drink during pregnancy' was the message of a massive publicity campaign launched by the American National Institute on Alcohol Abuse and Alcoholism (NIAAA).

This followed the first official government warning that alcohol could damage the foetus. The US Surgeon General issued a statement in July 1981 advising women who are pregnant or considering pregnancy not only to abstain from alcohol, but to 'be aware of the alcoholic content of food and drugs'.

Rather than trying to draw the line at a certain level of drinking, some medical experts say we should regard alcohol as potentially damaging in any case and this damage as increasing by degree.

There is no 'threshold effect' of safety for any teratogen (any substance which can damage the foetus) yet studied in humans, according to Dr David Smith.[17] None of these substances are safe to a particular level and dangerous only beyond that.

Various eminent American researchers have been saying for years that pregnant women, to be safe, should *not drink at all*. Dr

Ruth Little, Director of the Alcoholism and Drug Abuse Institute at the University of Washington, says that regular social drinking (two or more drinks daily) is linked with retarded growth of the foetus and behavioural problems in the baby – as well as low birth weight and stillbirth.[19]

In Britain the Royal College of Physicians gave their opinion in 1987 that for women who are pregnant – or planning to be – 'it is probably sensible . . . to abstain from alcohol, or at least to restrict their consumption to an occasional drink, especially in the early stages of pregnancy.'[20]

Aversions

For some women 'safe limits' is never an issue: they simply cannot face alcohol when pregnant. Many women suffer from nausea (usually connected to a healthy pregnancy) and feel too sick to drink. At the same time, some women lose all desire for cigarettes and coffee, substances which can also be bad for the foetus.

The biological reason for these aversions is not fully understood, but 'pregnancy is the only life event' writes Dr Ruth Little, '(for either males or females) associated with a spontaneous, predictable and substantial decrease in alcohol use'. Even heavy drinkers tend to drink less when they get pregnant – and, again according to Dr Little, they tend to cut down even before they realize they are pregnant.[21]

But cutting down on drinking is very difficult for women who are dependent on alcohol, whether they are pregnant or not. All the more reason for education about the risks of drinking, long before women even think of having a baby.

In perspective

We don't know which groups of women are most at risk during pregnancy in the UK, although it is well established that smoking, poverty and low social class increase a baby's chance of being born small and of dying in the perinatal period (from the seventh month of pregnancy to the first week of life). Working-class women have a higher chance of having smaller babies and babies who will die from malformations than middle-class women.[22]

The risks to the foetus from alcohol have to be seen in the context of this much greater overall problem of poverty. Foresight, the association for the promotion of pre-conceptual care, estimate that between 6 and 10 per cent of all children have some disability at the age of five years. They claim that up to half of these arise in the perinatal period and could have been prevented.[23]

Alcohol is just one of the 'social poisons' responsible for this tragic toll, which could have been reduced through education, good nutrition and protection from pollutants – as well as through avoiding cigarettes and alcohol. Many factors in western life combine to deplete our bodies of essential vitamins and trace minerals. This 'hidden malnutrition' – not always evident in the parents – places the foetus at risk, say Foresight. Zinc, for example, is important to a foetus's healthy development, but alcohol consumption (as well as the contraceptive pill, copper piping in soft-water areas, the refining and processing of foods and the use of chemical fertilizers) cheats our bodies of it.[24]

Foresight has also been one of the few groups to say that the father's health in the conception of a healthy foetus has been too long overlooked, although it is a principle well established in farming and animal breeding. So far the emphasis has been on a mother's responsibility for a healthy pregnancy and she is made to carry the burden of guilt for any failures. But Foresight say *both* parents should ideally be well nourished and free from toxic substances, such as alcohol, before they try to conceive.

The personal, social and economic costs of disability are high, but the suffering of mother and child, and the tragedy of lost potential for FAS children can never be calculated. Until the government decides to make education and prevention a priority, it is a tragedy which will continue.

9

HANGOVERS: 'THE WRATH OF GRAPES'

The hangover is not simply a physical state which follows overindulgence in alcohol. For some drinkers it has a semi-mystical significance – it is their badge of boozing courage, and is almost as important as getting drunk. But for others it is an occasion for excruciating guilt, remorse and sickness, the stigma of shameful behaviour.

Women (see chapters 1 and 2) are particularly prone to regrets about loss of control and waste of time.

Men, far more than women, are likely to get a kick out of their hangovers, just as they are usually more proud of their drinking exploits. The hangover, especially amongst a group of men who have been drinking together, brings with it a kind of macho, locker-room spirit, the camaraderie of battle survivors. Men who have gone 'over the top' together are inclined to relish their shared symptoms the next morning, comparing the state of their heads, stomachs and bowels.

David Outerbridge has written *The Hangover Handbook* in this vein, and it is full of jokey anecdotes, caricatures of men with big noses and squiffy eyes, and 'cures' – such as this one from Kingsley Amis:[1] 'Upon awakening: If your wife or other partner is beside you, and (of course) is willing, perform the sexual act as vigorously as you can. The exercise will do you good, and – on the assumption that you enjoy sex – you will feel toned-up emotionally.'

In the same spirit is a quote from the notorious drinking 'hero' W. C. Fields as he refuses a chaser of water: 'Watah – fish fuck in water.' Fields's hangover cure is more booze – a martini of one part vermouth and four parts of gin, 'to be taken around the clock'. And it is not only our culture that finds the hangover funny. David Outerbridge translates the phrases used in other countries to show how evocative the expressions can be:

French: *gueule de bois*, snout of wood
German: *Katzenjammer*, a wailing of cats
Norwegian: *jeg har tommermenn*, I have carpenters in my head
Italian: *stonato*, out of tune
Portuguese: *ressaca*, literally undertow, or line of surf, or 'the
   tide has gone out'.[2]

His own description has all the masochistic gusto of the true hangover connoisseur:

The head is an urn of complaints. Most immediate is a hammering headache that is both dull and intense simultaneously. To move the head causes new pains at the back of the skull, and to open the eyes sends shafts of painful light in the front. The ears ring and outside noises are unusually abrasive. The mouth is dry and feels caked. The taste is terrible and breath feels foul (and is). The tongue and throat are parched, the chest is taut with heartburn, and any attempt to move causes severe dizziness. This sensation of queasiness immediately telegraphs itself to the stomach which is entertaining its own disorders. The dizziness compounds a feeling of general nausea; sometimes this will surge into a fit of vomiting, but more often will continue to hold the victim in a limbo of wooziness and diarrhoea, and a desire for a cathartic heave. In addition, the stomach walls have been scoured by the alcohol, producing true indigestion. The nervous system is still drugged, causing the body to experience uncontrolled shakes: this is most noticeable in the hands, but the flushes of the face and the chills of the torso are allied manifestations.

The author is showing off, but habitual drinkers will recognize some of these disorders.

In more prosaic terms the symptoms of a hangover can include digestive upsets (vomiting, loss of appetite, heartburn), emotional upsets (anxiety, depression), thirst, weakness, headache, sweating, giddiness, general shakiness and tremor of the eyeballs, palpitations, and fatigue.

This is how your body makes its protest when you have inflicted too much drink upon it. Alcohol is directly poisonous to the tissues and your body can only eliminate it at a constant rate. If you drink too much and/or too fast you will 'overload' it and the ill effects of alcohol will accumulate.

And in addition to the toxic effects of alcohol, the body has to cope with other impurities in alcoholic drinks called congeners. These are substances which may derive from yeasts, sugars, flavourings and colourings in alcoholic beverages. The closer your type of drink is to pure alcohol, the less congeners it should contain. Vodka for instance is purer than bourbon whisky, and white wine has less congeners than red wine.

It is thought that a number of hangover symptoms are the result of allergic reactions to congeners[3] and it is worth bearing this in mind if you are counting your drinks in terms of units. The alcohol content of six units of beer (three pints) will be the same as the alcohol content of six units of red wine (six glasses). The damage done by the alcohol will be the same for both drinks, but you may feel worse if you drink the wine, as a result of the different congeners.

Symptoms

Hangover symptoms vary considerably according to the individual, the kind of drink taken, how much of it you consume and how accustomed you are to drinking. Hangovers can be worse during a period because alcohol inhibits the formation of folic acid, which is important in the formation of red blood cells. Combined with the loss of iron through menstrual bleeding, this results in lethargy and tiredness. And the lowest common denominator of the hangover is probably tiredness.

Tiredness: You could be tired simply because you were drinking until the small hours and got up early, and so haven't had enough time asleep.

But if you go to bed drunk, the quality of your sleep is poor anyway and you are likely to wake up unrefreshed. This is because you have missed vital Rapid Eye Movement (REM) sleep, so called because the eyes move rapidly under the lids, 'watching' the events of your dreams.

Studies have shown that for our physical and mental health we all need to experience this form of 'dreaming' sleep. Without it, people can become extremely irritable and anxious.

REM sleep normally occurs four or five times a night for periods of half an hour. But for this to happen the higher brain needs to be very active and if it has been 'numbed' by alcohol (or sleeping pills) you cannot have REM sleep until the anaesthetic effect has worn off. This can take several hours – depending on how much you have consumed, and so the value of your sleep is less than you might normally expect.

Some drinkers try to sleep long into the morning to make up for their lost dreaming time, but it is a common complaint of hangover victims that they wake up feeling anxious and guilty at the crack of dawn and can't get back to sleep.

Your fatigue from a poor sleep is likely to be further aggravated by sheer bodily tiredness, the results of overdoing it while drunk the night before. It is a common pattern to feel tired in the evening after a busy day, and to have a few drinks to perk you up. With this new-found but artificial energy (the drink has numbed the parts of the brain which register physical discomfort and weariness), you go on drinking. If you feel sufficiently revived you might go on to a party – drinking, talking, dancing and generally over-exerting yourself. You feel the effects of this the next day as the alcoholic anaesthesia wears off, the pain centres of the brain wake up and your body feels as if you had put it through a wringer.

Headache: You are also likely to have a headache. This could be a consequence of tiredness, of dehydration or of falling asleep in an awkward position. It could also be an allergic reaction to the congeners found in drinks like port, sherry or red wine.

According to David Outerbridge, the brain cell walls have adapted to alcohol by becoming more sensitive - hence the hyper-sensitivity of your head on the morning after. He says the solution is to allow the brain cells to return to normal, by taking a small quantity of alcohol or 'the hair of the dog'. This avoids the 'abrupt, disquieting shock' of the return to normal and the consequent headache.[4] This is a popular theory in the macho tradition, but one which conflicts with the arguments of the medical specialists, who say that most of all your body now needs a complete rest from alcohol. Fighting booze with booze is a dangerous practice, and if you reach the stage where only drink can alleviate your hangover symptoms you are entering the vicious circle of alcohol dependence.

Thirst: Habitual drinkers will be familiar with another sure sign of having overdone it - waking up in the night or morning with a raging thirst.

This happens partly because alcohol, by acting on the hormones which control production of urine, makes you urinate more than usual. But alcohol also alters the distribution of water in your body, pulling liquid out of the cells and increasing the amount of extra-cellular fluid. The thirst you feel is in response to the need to replenish your body cells.

You can stave off some of the ill effects of dehydration by drinking plenty of water before you go to sleep.

Digestive upsets: Swallow too much of anything and your stomach will rebel; alcohol is no exception. How much is too much, your insides are likely to signal to you at the time – which is why vomiting plays a large part in drinking stories, especially for beginner drinkers.

If you are a regular drinker the ill effects are less likely to make themselves felt until the following morning. Queasiness is consequently a common hangover symptom. The prospect of putting food into your ravaged stomach is repulsive, and if your hangover is severe you may vomit when you get moving in the morning.

Even after vomiting you may still feel nauseous and bilious, or suffer an attack of the dreaded 'dry heaves', in which you go through the motions of vomiting but nothing happens because your stomach is empty. You may not be able to face food for some time.

If you resort to drink as a 'cure', or start drinking again before replenishing your body with food and allowing your digestive tract to recover, you are likely to upset the mechanisms of appetite and nutrition and suffer from vitamin deficiency. Chronic drinking eventually interferes with the process of digesting and absorbing food and chronic gastritis can be the result. Continuous stomach upsets are one of the warning signs of problem drinking.

Emotional upsets: As unpleasant as the physical symptoms of a hangover can be, they are bearable, to some extent treatable and you know that in time they will pass. But the mental and emotional suffering that can accompany a hangover is a far more distressing experience.

Guilt, depression, remorse, shame and self-accusation often comprise the legacy of a drinking bout. When this happens the hangover sufferer wakes up in the morning (probably at dawn and racked with anxiety), recalls what happened the night before and swears never to touch another drop. For reasons already described, this is more likely to happen to women than to men.

For men, the hangover can be simply the consequence of sociable masculine behaviour, the mark of being 'one of the lads', and nothing to be ashamed of. But for women, getting drunk is not generally socially acceptable. Drunken behaviour in women is frowned upon, associated with 'promiscuity' and 'unfeminine' comportment. The drunk woman may have escaped these strictures for as long as she is drinking, but when she is sober again and physically unwell from the hangover – all the weight of social and internalized condemnation descends on her head.

It is also generally true that women have more to *do* than men. The division between work and leisure time doesn't exist in many women's lives – either because their work *is* in the home, or because their work continues in the home when they return from their paid jobs. For women then, 'wasting time' with a hangover is a more serious and guilt-ridden business than it is for most men.

You may also have said or done things when drunk which you later regret and so feel guilty or ashamed. If you are one of those people who swear to go on the wagon after every binge, you will be further depressed by the 'failure' to keep your resolutions – especially if your drinking upsets other people who are close to you.

But if you do feel depressed and upset after a drinking bout, try to remember that your physiological state is also magnifying your emotional pain. Anxiety and depression are well-recognized symptoms of heavy drinking, and the way you feel about yourself could be as much a consequence of chemical changes in your body, as of what you have done or said.

Take some rest and concentrate on getting your body back into shape before examining your conscience too rigorously. And try to put your social embarrassment into the context of the double standard for men and women drinkers.

Prevention and cure

The only sure way to prevent a hangover is – don't drink. But if you want to drink, or think you might be put in a social situation where it is difficult to refuse, there are several things you can do to make the following day easier for yourself:

– Try to drink slowly, sipping instead of gulping drinks. If you arrive at the pub or party feeling very parched, quench your thirst first with a few soft drinks before starting on alcohol.

– Try to keep your consumption down to one unit of alcohol (i.e. one glass of wine or half a pint of beer) per hour. By drinking more or faster than this you are likely to become increasingly intoxicated until you abandon all the good resolutions of your sober self – and feel the consequences in the morning.

– Eat something, preferably fatty or oily food or drink milk, before you start drinking alcohol. The food will line the walls of your stomach and intestine, slowing the rate of absorption of alcohol.

– Stop drinking alcohol several hours before you are expecting to go to sleep and have another snack of food and drink some water, fruit juice or other soft drinks. Freshly squeezed lemon juice in water is said to counteract the harmful effects of alcohol on the liver. If you are feeling queasy, take some liver salts before going to bed.

There are many old adages about the dangers of drinking different types of alcohol in one sitting ('Don't mix the grape and the grain'), and some of the worst hangovers strike after all the beer or wine has run out and people start drinking whatever else they can lay their hands on, usually spirits.

On these occasions it is probably the sheer quantity of alcohol consumed that does most of the damage, but most drinkers agree that it is safer to stick to one kind of drink.

It is a well-established custom, however, to mix drinks, starting with an aperitif, then wine, etc. on stylish occasions structured around a meal. In this case the small dose of each drink, the length of time taken over the meal and the food itself, help blot up the ill-effects.

– Sleep for as long as you can to make up for those lost hours of refreshing REM sleep. If you do wake up early feeling anxious, try to go back to sleep if you can. It sometimes helps to get up for a while and have a hot drink and a bath. Or do something 'virtuous' like tidying up – and then go back to bed. If you can't sleep during the morning, make sure your next night is an early one.

Cures

The search for the hangover miracle cure has yielded countless remedies, recipes and potions. Some of these are common sense; others are plain harmful.

The only sure remedy is to stop drinking alcohol, drink plenty of fluids, get some rest and *wait*. You have put poisons into your body and you must give it time to recover. But in the meantime there are things you can do to make yourself feel better.

– Painkillers, like aspirin, will help your headache or other aches, but might also further irritate your stomach. You can avoid this by sticking to the soluble brands.

– Replenish your body with vitamins and minerals. Alcohol can eventually deplete the body's store of minerals such as magnesium, calcium and potassium. Lack of magnesium can cause cramps and spasms and irritability of the nerves and muscles. A dose of liver salts or magnesium sulphate will help remedy this deficiency.

Lack of potassium can cause tremors. Eat oranges and tomatoes to make up for this. For calcium, drink milk and eat cheese, sardines, herrings, flour and watercress.

Alcohol also runs down your supply of vitamins B_1, B_6 and C. Foods rich in the B vitamins are wholemeal bread, yeast, dairy products and meats like liver and bacon. Vitamin C is best taken in the form of citrus fruits or their juices, green vegetables, blackcurrants and new potatoes. B and C vitamins can usually be bought in tablet form, and it is quite a good idea for regular drinkers to take these as a matter of course.

– Fresh air and exercise can help you to feel better generally by getting your blood circulation moving so that reviving oxygen is carried around the body. (A whiff of pure oxygen is also said to work wonders, but is not available to most of us.)

– Psychologically, exercise can be especially helpful. You will feel you are doing something healthy to make up for the damage inflicted on your body – and the activity helps to relieve stress and calm the nerves if you are suffering from hangover guilt.

But don't overdo it; you are likely to be tired and your body might get more benefit from rest. The type of exercise which gets the circulation going and relaxes without exhausting you, like yoga or some gentle swimming, is ideal.

– There are some so-called cures which might give you an instant lift, but which won't do you any good in the long run. Coffee, for instance, will help wake you up and slake your thirst, and it is soothing as a hot drink. But it is no more a miraculous remedy for a hangover than it is a good way to sober up. Strong coffee especially can make you even more anxious and jittery when your nerves are bad, and it can make stomach acidity worse.

Again, many hardened drinkers swear by the 'hair of the dog' – another dose of alcohol. But this habit has probably helped them to become hardened drinkers in the first place. A couple of drinks on the morning after – if you can face them – might well make you feel better *temporarily*. The alcohol will anaesthetize some of your painful symptoms, and in topping up your blood alcohol level again, you are averting the unpleasantness of withdrawal from the drug.

But this is *not* an advisable practice. Your liver and other organs need time to recover before they face another onslaught of alcohol. And the more you drink the more your level of tolerance is likely to rise, and the higher your chances of becoming a dangerously dependent drinker. In the long run it will be much better for you to ride out the withdrawal symptoms or alleviate them with some of the above methods.

Some doctors say you should abstain altogether for several days – and others say weeks – before taking any more drink on board.

Part Three

COPING WITH DRINKING PROBLEMS

10

DO YOU HAVE A DRINKING PROBLEM?

We have a whole range of words to describe the use and abuse of alcohol such as 'heavy' drinking, 'moderate' and 'social' drinking, 'chemical dependency', 'problem' drinking and 'alcoholism'. They are morally weighted and ill-defined words: a judgement is implicit in each of them, and my idea of a heavy drinker might be your idea of an alcoholic, or vice versa. These days, the term 'alcoholic' is increasingly unpopular (except with people who follow the ideas of Alcoholics Anonymous), while 'chemical dependency' is used more often by the private agencies to describe the range of problems which they tackle.

Yet the imprecise nature of these terms reflects the variable and shifting nature of drinking patterns and problems. To be a drinker is to stand somewhere on a continuum: at one extreme is problem-free abstinence, at the other is the complex of drinking problems sometimes called 'alcoholism'.

What does 'alcoholism' mean? – the long-standing debate

The argument about the meaning of 'alcoholism' has been a long and heated one. Politicians, brewers, social workers, doctors, drinkers, all have some kind of interest in the 'correct' definition – and so the debate goes on. Different theories have held sway at different times, and have had a crucial effect on the treatment of people with alcohol problems.

In recent decades in this country, the concept of alcoholism as a *disease* prevailed, and alcoholics were the domain of the medical profession. It was generally believed that the reasons a person got into trouble with alcohol were due to that individual's biochemistry or personality. 'Alcoholics' were thought to have some abnormality which made them unable to control their drinking, so that abstinence was the only 'cure'. (Alcoholics Anonymous [AA], has remained faithful to this idea, their members attempting to 'get sober' permanently, yet continuing to call themselves alcoholics – people who are 'allergic' to alcohol.)

The disease concept helped to lighten the burden of moral judgement against 'alcoholics' who had in previous times been condemned for weakness and sinfulness, and justified their treatment as people who needed support and rehabilitation rather than punishment. But this theory was limited: it implied that there could be one explanation for all alcohol problems. However, years of research has come up with no evidence of any single personality or biochemical factor that alone could cause alcohol problems.

In recent years, increasing recognition has been given to the relationship between alcohol problems and the per capita consumption of alcohol in any population. It was found that those societies which drank the most also had the most problem drinkers and the most deaths from cirrhosis. Drink problems were attributed to the amount consumed in any society. But this theory again left out certain important questions. Why, for instance, did some people and not others in the same society come to grief through alcohol?

Opinion in the alcohol field is still divided. Broadly speaking, there are two main camps. One takes the medical model, talks about 'alcoholism' as a disease, and recommends abstinence as a 'cure'. The other stresses the social context of drinking and believes that 'problem drinkers' (rather than 'alcoholics'), can learn to control their drinking without necessarily abstaining.

But the years of dispute have led to a consensus that alcohol dependency is a highly complex phenomenon with no single cause or 'cure'. The evidence of recent years is that there are many different factors – social, economic, psychological and physiological – involved in problem drinking. This wide range of factors affects why, what and when we drink, and also how much harm will result.

Authorities like the World Health Organization now tend to avoid the term 'alcoholism' and use 'dependence on alcohol' or 'alcohol-dependence syndrome'. The term alcoholism is widely felt to be unsatisfactory as it implies one disease instead of the many types of alcohol abuse which exist, and the range of problems which lie behind them.

Where the term is still used, it is used for convenience and is broadly defined: 'Repeated consumption of alcohol leading to dependence, physical disease or other harm' is a typical definition.' Alcoholism is seen as a condition not only related to the amounts of drink consumed; also important is the drinker's social background, health, diet, work and pattern of drinking.

Workers in the alcohol field now seem less concerned with precise definitions than with the practical implications of the terminology. For instance, some say they find 'alcoholism' useful in describing extreme drinking problems; others avoid it because of the stigma attached. For women in particular the label 'alcoholic' can be damaging, further lowering a woman's self-esteem and discouraging her from coming forward for treatment. ACCEPT has argued that calling a person 'alcoholic' confirms her in a 'loser's role' which she may have subconsciously chosen, and so perpetuates her drinking problems.

And unless 'alcoholism' is understood in its full complexity, its causes cannot effectively be tackled. 'A treatment approach which is narrowly conceived in terms of such simple propositions as, for example, alcoholism is *always* rooted in personality disorder, *always* due to lack of social skills, or *always* the result of loneliness, is likely to be inadequate and misconceived.'[2]

The prevailing theory

In recent years, opinion in the alcohol field has moved towards a multi-dimensional approach. Factors of class, sex and race greatly affect our drinking patterns. Current understanding of alcohol problems follows broadly along these lines: Initially, the pattern of our drinking is affected by cultural attitudes. In some cultures drinking is seen as 'manly' behaviour, whereas in others it is forbidden. In our society, drinking is accepted by the majority as a sociable form of behaviour for adults, but drunkenness is less acceptable, especially in women.

We learn to drink within this framework of 'informal social controls',[3] and under varying degrees of social pressure we develop our drinking 'habit'. There are certain high-risk occupations (such as bar work) and groupings (young males), in which the pressure to drink is especially strong.

Having a parent with drink problems also significantly increases our chances of developing problems – and forming a relationship with someone who has a drink problem. Both the environmental effect of 'learned behaviour' from parents who we see using booze to 'cope' with their difficulties, and hereditary factors, contribute to this. As yet there is no definite evidence that a physical predisposition to alcohol dependence can be inherited. It does seem likely, however, that a genetic susceptibility which makes individuals more vulnerable to the effects of alcohol could be one of the many factors involved in drinking problems.[4]

Depression can also lead to the drinker developing problems (although not much is known about this). Women, for instance, are more likely than men to turn to professional counsellors, therapists, and anti-depressant drugs when they feel distressed. Men are more likely to resort to alcohol than seek professional help. And the more education you have, the more likely you are to seek professional help rather than the short-term benefits of alcohol.[5]

Below a certain level of drinking, no physical dependency should develop, but psychological dependency can develop after a period (several years or even months) of having a regular drink. We feel we 'need' a drink when it comes to our usual time for having one. If we don't have one we feel as uncomfortable as a smoker who is trying to give up cigarettes. But at this stage there would be no physical withdrawal symptoms if we did give up. This psychological dependence reinforces our learned habit, and the more we drink, the stronger these factors become.

The extent of drinking at this level is also affected by the price and availability of drink. If you have enough spare cash, if you work in a traditionally boozy job, if the price of drink is low and the pub opening hours long, you are likely to drink more than you would under different circumstances.

Eventually alcohol's properties as a drug which induces physical dependence begin to take effect, and your body's response to alcohol becomes different from what it was initially. It is now thought that anybody, under certain circumstances, could become physically dependent on alcohol, but the major factors are how much a person drinks and for how long.

Although the critical amount varies from one individual to another, physical dependence (and chronic physical damage) can develop in a woman when she is consuming four units of alcohol or more each day, according to Dr John Saunders of King's College Hospital Liver Unit. Physical dependence is, however, 'unusual' below six units but women can become physically damaged without developing dependence.

Once the drinker has become dependent it takes more and more alcohol to achieve the same level of intoxication, and without continuous doses of drink she or he will suffer withdrawal symptoms such as shakiness, sweating and anxiety. Below is a list of the symptoms of alcohol dependence in the order in which they most commonly occur:[6]

Completely unable to keep to a drink limit
Need more drink than companions (i.e. going for drink
    between rounds)

Difficulty preventing getting drunk
Spending more time drinking
Missing meals drinking
'Blackouts', memory loss
Giving up interests because drinking interferes
Restless without a drink
Changes to drinking same on working days as on days off
Organizing day to ensure supply
Change to drinking same amounts whatever mood
Passing out from drink in public
Trembling after drinking the day before
Times when can't think of anything except getting a drink
Morning retching or vomiting
Sweating excessively at night
Withdrawal fit
Morning drinking
Decreased tolerance
Waking up panicking or frightened
Hallucinations

Unfortunately, it is a well-known characteristic of developing alcohol dependence that the drinker tends to deny that any problem exists. The drinking continues and increases as long as health and circumstances permit.

Anger, threats, pleas and accusations can often have no effect other than reinforcing the drinker's sense of isolation and guilt, and adding to the 'reasons' for drinking. All too often it takes a major disaster – a partner leaving, getting the sack, or health collapsing – before she or he seeks treatment.

Tackling the problem

Most professional treatment agencies have traditionally been geared to dealing with the results only of extreme drinking problems. Alcoholics Anonymous, too, is generally a last resort for 'alcoholics'. Few organizations offer help *before* major damage is done (with exceptions like Drinkwatchers, see below), although in recent years more alcohol advice and counselling services are running public campaigns to try to catch people at earlier stages of a drink problem.

This is partly because denial is a common factor in drinking problems, and partly because the 'responsible' bodies in this country (some of which have vested interests in *not* reducing alcohol consumption, see chapter 6) put so few resources into prevention and education.

Women who fear they are developing, or could develop, alcohol problems will also have difficulty in finding an established agency geared to their needs. DRINKLINE , the national alcohol helpline set up in 1993 receives many calls from women who can't or don't want to, approach an agency for help. If this is your situation, you may decide that self-help is your best option.

Self-help

As the all-women groups run by professional workers have shown (see chapter 11), we can gain enormously from joint discussion and mutual support. Our sense of guilt over drinking can be alleviated in a group where other women feel they have been drinking too much, or admit that they too have taken to drinking secretly or hiding bottles around the house.

And as there is no way of understanding the reasons why we drink without becoming aware of our situation as women in society, self-help groups can help us to identify common areas of discontent and frustration as a first step towards dealing with them – without depending on drink.

You may want to organize your group amongst friends, or through a local women's centre. Alternatively, try putting an advertisement in the free listings of a magazine.

I would suggest four main areas of discussion for a drinkers' self-help group: why do you drink? how much do you drink?

what kind of drinker are you? and strategies for cutting down.

*   *   *

Why do you drink?: The group could talk about reasons for drink in general terms. Do you abuse alcohol when you are feeling shy or angry, frustrated or lonely, or when under stress? If so, what are the circumstances and situations which make you feel this way? Try to work out new ways of coping with stress (such as exercise or yoga), or techniques of avoiding it (perhaps assertiveness training).

How much do you drink?: Work out how much you are in the habit of drinking. Add up the number of drinks you have had every day for a typical week, using the basic unit of one for a glass of wine or sherry, a pub tot of spirits or half a pint of beer or lager. (Cans of special-strength lager count as three units each.)

This unit system is a convenient way of working out the alcohol content of whatever you are drinking, and the damage done by the alcohol in four units of whisky and four units of beer will be the same. Bear in mind, however, that some drinks have additional dangers. If you drink spirits, especially at home, you are likely to pour larger measures than you would get in a pub, and do yourself more harm. And you can drink whisky much faster than beer and so get more drunk, more quickly. Beer, however, is unit-for-unit more fattening than spirits, which can make for further health and emotional problems. And some drinks, such as red wine, have more congeners and may give you worse hangovers.

Don't be discouraged if your total of units seems alarmingly high at first, or higher than anyone else's. Cutting down can be a slow process, so give yourself credit for every bit of progress.

Your eventual target should be about fourteen units a week, or two units a day, or even less. Try not to drink every day; 'days off' in between drinking give your body time to recover and replenish itself.

What kind of drinker are you?: The following questions (based on a London Council on Alcoholism questionnaire), are designed to help you assess your drinking pattern in terms of dependency and vulnerability to problems. Put a tick against the statements which are true, or closest to the truth for you. Tick one for each category, and then add up your score as shown below:

1. *If I was advised to give up drinking for the sake of my health –*
a. I could do so easily
b. I could do so but I'd miss it
c. I could do so but with difficulty
d. I could only do so if I had help
e. I don't think I could do it

2. *This time last year my favourite drink was –*
a. stronger than what I drink now
b. weaker than what I drink now
c. the same as what I drink now

3. *When I am drinking with my friends I notice that –*
a. they seem to drink about the same speed that I do
b. they drink faster than I do
c. some of them drink slower than I do

d. most of them drink slower than I do
If you answered yes to a or b, then also answer the following:
My new friends tend to
e. drink faster than my old friends
f. drink slower than my old friends

4. *Where I buy my drink –*
a. I have a credit account
b. I do not have a credit account
If you answered yes to a, then also answer the following:
The amount that I owe on my credit account is –
c. generally about what I would expect
d. sometimes rather more than I'd expected

5. *I usually first think about drinking –*
a. when I wake up
b. sometime during the morning

c. at lunchtime
d. late in the afternoon
e. in the evening
If you answered yes to a, b, or c,
then also answer the following:
When I plan the rest of
my day –
f. drinking is a high priority
g. drinking is not particularly
   important to me

6. *Before going to a social event –*
a. I never have a drink
b. I seldom have a drink
c. I usually have a drink

7. *When I decide whether to go to*
a social event –
a. it doesn't matter to me
   whether or not alcohol is
   going to be available there
b. I prefer some drink to be
   available there
c. I don't really enjoy it
   unless some drink is going
   to be available
d. I will only attend if I know
   drink will be available
   there

8. *After I have had a few*
drinks –

a. I never pretend to have
   had less than I really have
b. I occasionally do pretend
   that
c. I often do pretend that
d. I sometimes declare I've
   had one more drink than
   I've actually had

9. *When it gets towards closing*
time –
a. I find I've had enough to
   drink
b. I tend to double my final
   order or buy some to take
   home with me

10. *In the course of everyday*
conversation my friends –
a. seldom talk about
   drinking
b. quite often talk about
   drinking
If you answered yes to b, then
also answer the following –
I have noticed that my friends
usually –
c. joke about it
d. offer some kind of advice
   to me
e. talk about drinking much
   more than me

Add up your score as follows and then assess yourself according to
the following 'categories':

1. a = 1, b = 1, c = 2, d = 3, e = 4

2. a = 1, b = 3, c = 2

3. a = 1, b = 1, c = 2, d = 3, e = 4, f = 2

4. a = 2, b = 1, c = 1, d = 2

5. a = 4, b = 3, c = 2, d = 1, e = 1, f = 3, g = 1

6. a = 1, b = 2, c = 3

7. a = 1, b = 2, c = 3, d = 4

8. a = 1, b = 3, c = 4, d = 2

9. a = 1, b = 3

10. a = 1, b = 2, c = 3, d = 4, e = 1

Relax: If you scored 17 or under you are not a dependent drinker and have no need to worry at present about your drinking habits. But don't forget that drinking habits can change, particularly in times of stress, and you may not *stay* a non-dependent drinker.

Be wary: If you scored from 18 to 24 you are likely to be a regular, but moderate drinker. You may feel a 'need' to drink now and then, and may be causing yourself harm – or causing others difficulties – from time to time.

You are in the area of mildly vulnerable drinking, and should watch your consumption carefully for signs of drinking more, or more often. If your friends say that you are starting to drink more, take heed: remember that it is easy to move along the continuum towards the problem end of drinking.

Cut down: If you scored 25 to 30, you are probably drinking regularly and drinking too much for the good of your health and relationships. You may not notice the 'need' to drink – because you are rarely going without it. You are now running a very high risk of developing more serious drink problems, so try to cut down the amount you drink, and to drink less often.

Seek help: If you scored over 31 you are probably dependent, physically and psychologically, on alcohol. You are certainly harming yourself and could be causing suffering to others.

If you stop drinking or try to cut down you may experience

unpleasant withdrawal symptoms (trembling, sweating, feelings of panic), and may feel confused, moody or depressed. As time goes on you will need more and more alcohol to reach the same level of intoxication. You should seek help from one of the organizations listed at the end of this chapter.

Strategies for cutting down

Here are some suggestions to help you cut down on your drinking, which can be adapted freely according to your taste or situation.

– Don't drink until a specific time in the day which you set for yourself, preferably to coincide with or to follow your evening meal.

– Don't drink at lunchtime. It will make you feel low in the afternoon as your blood sugar level sinks and the depressant effect follows the 'high'. You will probably feel tense as a result and feel the need to repeat the 'lift'. Sugary tea or food will raise your blood sugar level again – a better alternative to more alcohol.

– Alternate alcohol with soft drinks. This is a useful trick for parties or tense social situations when you feel nervous or under pressure.

– Don't allow your glass to be topped up until you have finished what is in it already. A lot of people keep drinking because they feel the need to do something with their hands in social situations, but there is a lot of comfort to be had from simply holding a glass.

– Arrange alternative activities in the times when you are in the habit of going to the pub. Relaxing activities like yoga or swimming will help you to unwind without alcohol. If you prefer more vigorous sports, beware the temptation to slake your thirst immediately afterwards with a few drinks. Drink fruit juice until you no longer feel thirsty.

– Make a pact with one or more friends that on given nights during the week you won't drink. Maybe you could meet and do something different with the money you have saved!

– Decide to stick to two non-drinking days a week – and tell people about your decision. Using the fourteen units a week ceiling, this allows you three units on other days – which feels like a reasonable amount.

– Make a rule for yourself only to drink in company.

– Never drink more than two units of alcohol (a pint of beer, two glasses of wine) in one hour.

– Always order singles or half pints. The whole process of buying and drinking half pints takes twice as long as buying pints, and so your drink will seem to last longer.

– Make a list of the number of calories in each type of drink – and absorb the information. Then when you feel like another, think to yourself: would I now have another two pieces of toast (or the equivalent of about 200 calories)? The answer will probably be *no*, and the psychological deterrent effect will put you off that next drink.

– If you feel a craving for a drink, try satisfying it with a tasty morsel of food instead. You will be surprised at how often food can give you the lift you need.

Professional helping agencies

If your drinking came into the 'seek help' category of the questionnaire above, you would be wise to ring the national telephone helpline DRINKLINE (0171 332 0202, 6-11pm daily).[1] Or, you could contact Alcohol Concern (0171 928 7377) for information about local alcohol advice services. Alcohol Concern publishes a Directory of Services in England and Wales which gives details of special services for women.

Alternatively, look up alcohol advice services under 'alcohol' in the phone book, or ask your local advice centre or citizen's advice bureau for a contact number.

There is a network of alcohol advice services across the country and an increasing number of these now have women counsellors and programmes for women drinkers. Many also offer support to relatives and friends of drinkers – if they don't, Alcohol Concern can tell you who does.

A good GP should, in theory, know about services, but all too often family doctors are ill-informed about alcohol problems. Since April 1993, however, under the Community Care reforms, you are entitled to go to your local social services and ask to be assessed for a drink problem.

Although Alcohol Concern does encourage people to take this course of action, there is evidence that mothers are avoiding contacting social services (who also have a child protection function) because they are afraid of losing their children into care if they admit to alcohol problems.

Women's special needs

The majority of alcohol advice services are mixed: 39 per cent of people using them are women. Most services these days do try to take account in some way of women's particular needs, for instance, by providing women-only groups, or offering the choice of a woman counsellor, or training staff in gender issues.

However, some services are better than others, and women's needs are often overlooked. Women in mixed groups are generally at a disadvantage as drinking women are considered more 'deviant' and 'difficult' than men. Men in groups are also inclined to judge women harshly, and women's contributions may be cast aside as men hold the floor and women reproduce their usual pattern of listening.[7]

Women workers in DAWN, and FARE (now merged into Alcohol Concern), have found that there is a 'myth of the aggressive woman drinker' which is related to the problem of homelessness.[8] Homelessness is often the main problem of women who start drinking after admission to hostels, but when women are offered decent accommodation their drinking usually decreases. So much do women drinkers dread the homeless state that they often stay in unsatisfactory relationships, or keep changing men, rather than stay in a hostel and become homeless.

As a result, homelessness for women drinkers is often a hidden problem. Workers in the alcohol field see so few homeless women that those they do see become more memorable. And, as homeless women, they are forced to compete for attention in male-dominated and male-oriented services.

Women also have special problems – beyond drinking – when they come to facilities for help. Many services lack creche facilities, so that mothers attending day care centres have nowhere to leave their children. Residential treatment can provide a vital space for a woman to recuperate, but, again, her children are rarely taken into account. And there is the fear for the mother that if she seeks treatment her children will be taken into care and subsequently kept from her.

In 1994 there were only seven residential services for women drinkers in the country. However, when the Community Care reforms came into force in April 1993, allocation of residential places became the job of social services and it appears that many women have backed off from asking for help as a result, fearing the loss of their children. Only two residential houses in the country also have places for children, enabling women to recover from drinking without traumatic family separations.

There are also difficulties for particular groups of women such as black women, lesbians, older women, and disabled women – who find that there are few services which cater to their needs. (However, see 'Women's Alcohol Centre', page 171.)

There is the further problem of labelling for women. Some services are based in psychiatric hospitals and so the woman – already stigmatized by the title 'alcoholic' – is now also labelled psychiatric patient'.

Available services

Below is a brief rundown of the type of services available in the UK. For more details of what is available in your area, contact Alcohol Concern for their Directory of Services.

Day centres: There are still not many of these across the country, but they are growing in number. Day Centres have a wide range of functions. Some are information and counselling centres; they offer a variety of activities for both individuals and groups. Others deal with homeless problem drinkers, referring them to hostels. They may be quite informal drop-in centres, or highly structured centres where you are required to attend regular activities.

Advice and counselling services (other than Councils on Alcohol): These will provide advice and counselling and may be useful as a starting point to tackle a drinking problem. Or their counselling facilities may see you through the problem altogether.

Alcohol Treatment Units (ATUs): These are run by the NHS in hospitals, and you may be referred as a day-patient or an inpatient by your GP or social worker. (If you don't think your GP is well informed, go to an advice centre first to enquire about ATUs, and then ask your GP to refer you.)

ATUs have facilities for 'detoxification' (coming off drink), and help you to cope with withdrawal effects, often with the use of drugs. They generally provide counselling, group work and social skills training as well.

Sadly, about half of all ATUs were axed or reduced in size during the 1980s. 'Home detox' has accordingly increased, with support from psychiatric nurses and doctors.

Residential facilities and hostels: These have living-in treatment programmes which may last from about six weeks to a year. They generally run groups and give counselling. They may help with job-hunting at the end of treatment, or finding accommodation for the homeless.

Psychiatric and General Hospitals: These may provide beds in their wards for alcohol-dependent patients on the same basis as ATUs. They may also take day-patients, and provide groups and counselling. Your GP will refer you for treatment.

Private facilities: These are usually residential and vastly expensive (around £1000 a week). They don't provide much more than the other facilities – except a richer class of problem drinker.

HM Services facilities: These exist for people in the armed forces, but some do take local people as well.

Community Alcohol Teams: These have been developed during the late 1980s so that there are now some 30 CATs around the country. Each team is likely to have a consultant psychiatrist, a couple of community psychiatric nurses, a probation officer, and a social worker plus members from the local counselling services. You can contact them directly (CATs may advertise their phone numbers or they may be in the phone book), or you may be referred to your local CAT - who then decide how best to help you.

Other groups

DRINKLINE: Perhaps the most welcome addition to alcohol services in recent years has been the national telephone helpline DRINKLINE, launched in August 1993. Sixty per cent of calls to the helpline, which is anonymous and confidential, have been from women. Many have called about the drinking of their partner, or of a close friend or relative.

'We have found that the taboos and double standards about women's drinking are as strong as ever,' says Sarah Berger, DRINKLINE's Director, 'and women drinkers hate themselves all the more because of them. Those who call about their own drinking are often consuming 70 or more units a week, and half have never sought help before. Many are professional and managerial women. Women are also being left with the burden of men's drinking.'

DRINKLINE is open every evening from 6pm until 11pm, including weekends. This makes it accessible to people who don't want to seek help during office hours, and to many women who may not be free to call in for counselling.

DRINKLINE's helpliners can offer support and advice to the family and friends of people with drink problems, or advise on where to get help in your own community. They can also give information about sensible drinking limits, drinking and driving and the effects of alcohol on the body.

Tel: 0171 332 0202, 6pm to 11pm, seven days a week.

Women's Alcohol Centre: Unlike other more traditional alcohol agencies, this one is tailor-made to the needs of women. The WAC was set up in London in 1984 to provide residential and day services specifically for women who are worried about their drinking. They have a Day Centre for women to drop in and get advice, plus two residential houses.

Their groups and workshops – including assertion, relaxation and a lesbian's group – reflect the need for women to see their drinking in a wide social context. WAC also offers complementary therapies, including acupuncture and art therapy and offers housing and legal advice.

Having a women-only facility has many advantages, say WAC, allowing women to look to their own needs instead of men's, encouraging women to talk freely, to identify with each other, to learn to like themselves as *women* – and to enjoy themselves together.

In addition, the WAC join in with other agencies who run groups for relatives of drinkers, and they do give counselling to relatives on an ad hoc basis. They also do couple counselling and have crèche and childcare facilities on request.

The WAC see many women whose children are considered 'at risk' by the social services because of their mothers' drinking. They also see women whose childrren are in care and can sometimes help to get the child back home.

An increasingly important development at WAC during the 1990s has been the growing parents' service. 'We have many women coming here who have young children, and they are worried about the effects of their own drinking on those children,' says the WAC's Director Anne McIntyre. 'We have a programme preparing mothers for the return of a child who may have been in care. We are also seeing more women who are victims of incest, rape and violence.' To date WAC regrets it is not wheelchair accessible, but they may be able to see women at other premises which are.

WAC are part of the wider Alcohol Recovery Project in London which has a range of drop-in/advice centres and residential projects. Contact the Women's Alcohol Centre at 66A Drayton Park, Islington N5 3ND. Tel. 0171-226 4581. Or, the ARP at Newington Causeway, London SE1 6DF. Tel. 0171-403 3369.

DAWN (Drugs and Alcohol Women's Network): was set up at the beginning of the 1980s to work for better understanding and treatment of drug and alcohol problems in women. It has come through some lean times to emerge as one of the most committed and significant groups putting the case for women in the alcohol field.

DAWN aims to provide women with accurate, non-sensationalized information, so that we can make our own choices about drug and alcohol use. It argues that society encourages women to be dependent on such things as tea, coffee, cigarettes, tranquillizers and husbands – but discourages us from dependency on anything that interferes with our role as mothers, workers or 'housewives' (such as alcohol or drugs). DAWN believes that the issues of women and dependency are related to women's position in society as well as to the particular drug involved.

DAWN provides advice and information for women as well as

publishing a range of information leaflets including leaflets for black women and workers in the community.

Contact DAWN at 30-31 Great Sutton Street, London EC1V 0DX. Tel: 0171 253 6221.

Alcohol Concern: This is a national charity set up in 1984 with central government funding which aims to promote safer drinking and reduce alcohol-related harm. Its main objectives are:

To raise public awareness of the risks of alcohol abuse.

To inform and educate people about the recommended limits for drinking.

To support and improve services for people with drink problems.

To promote action, locally and nationally, to prevent the harm caused by excess drinking.

Alcohol Concern wants to halve the number of people drinking more than the recommended limit. It wants an eventual ban on drink-driving, with random breath testing and lower blood alcohol limits in the meantime. It wants to see taxes on alcohol go up, as well as an improvement in helping services, and it operates a workplace advisory service advising employers and trade unions.

Alcohol Concern has a comprehensive library and resource centre with a wide range of publications.

Contact Alcohol Concern (Waterbridge House, 32-36 Loman Street, London SE1 0EE. Tel: 0171 928 7377) to find out about services in your area. Alcohol Concern say that half of the people who make contact asking for advice and help are women, seeking help either for themselves or for a drinking partner or relative.

Alcoholics Anonymous: AA is a world-wide network of mutual aid, support and self-help groups which now has one and three-quarter million members. There is no doubt that it has been enormously effective in helping huge numbers of 'alcoholics' to give up alcohol, and has saved innumerable lives in the process. However, the style and ideology of AA are not to everyone's taste.

AA group meetings take two basic forms. At open meetings, which anyone may attend, there is usually a chairperson and a speaker, and 'alcoholics' in the group will talk about their experiences. Closed meetings are for AA members only, to enable 'alcoholics' to discuss their problems amongst themselves.

The only requirement for AA membership is the desire to stop drinking, and there are no dues or membership fees. AA stays strictly non-aligned and non-sectarian.

The aim of members is to stay sober and to help others 'achieve sobriety'. The question of 'what is alcoholism?' is rarely discussed at AA, where the emphasis is on recovery from, rather than investigation into, the causes of alcohol problems.

The structure of the organization is non-hierarchical, with power lying in the groups rather than at the centre. Typically, AA's central body is called, *not* the Board of Directors, but the General Service Board.

AA uses very simple, gospel-type formulae, like the 'Twelve Traditions', the 'Three Legacies' and the 'Twelve Steps'. The latter, for instance, are steps intended to direct 'alcoholics' along the road to recovery and 'spiritual growth'. The First Step is to admit 'we were powerless over alcohol'. The Second Step is 'to believe that a Power greater than ourselves could restore us to sanity'. The other Steps encourage the practice of self-criticism, confession and reparation of past wrongs, surrender to God's will ('as we understand *Him* [my italics]'), prayer and meditation, and carrying the message to other 'alcoholics'.

AA claims to use spiritual rather than religious methods, and this process of moving from despair through confession to penance, hope and faith follows the pattern of various spiritual practices. AA members commonly talk in terms of 'conversion' to their new life.

These methods do work for many people who come to AA in a desperate, fearful and confused state. In its policy of avoiding all controversy, AA is not concerned with causes of problems or with working for social change.

And the organization itself – rather than alcohol – can become the structure on which the recovering drinker depends. 'I used to go to the pub every day; now I go to meetings every day,' said one member at an open meeting.

AA is resistant to the idea of women-only groups – and to any form of group that changes the criterion for membership from the simple 'desire to stop drinking'. However, women in registered AA groups can organize their own women's meetings. This is fairly widespread in the US, but there are only a handful of such groups in Britain.

And although its female membership has grown enormously to the present ratio of at least one woman to every three men, it remains essentially male-oriented. The AA 'bible', *Alcoholics Anonymous*, includes a chapter called 'To Wives', but there isn't one addressed to husbands.

The groups do vary widely in character according to location and luck, and, for many drinkers with severe problems, it is the best available solution. Local groups are often listed in telephone directories, or contact the national office at P.O. Box 1, Stonebow House, Stonebow, York YO1 2NJ. Tel. 01904 644026.

Coping with a drinker in the family: In this book I have focused chiefly on alcohol's effects on women *as drinkers*, but of course we are also vastly affected by other people's drinking problems, especially within a family unit (see chapter 12). Alcohol dependency is often called 'the family illness', and much of the literature suggests that marital conflict, poor parent-child relationships, social isolation and communication problems are characteristic of families of both men and women with drinking problems.[9]

If you are living with a problem drinker, you are likely to need help and support yourself. Some local alcohol agencies have relatives' groups, and the private clinics also tend to run groups for 'co-dependents' (partners, relatives or friends of problem drinkers).

The biggest network to help those affected by problem drinkers, however, is the Al-Anon family groups. Al-Anon say that as many as four million people in the UK and Ireland are seriously affected because someone close to them has a drinking problem – and that these people could be helped by Al-Anon (or the young people's group, Al-Ateen) whether or not the drinker in their lives recognizes that a problem exists.

Al-Anon family groups follow much the same pattern of meetings and philosophy as Alcoholics Anonymous, and you tend to find (mostly) husbands going to the local AA meetings, while (mostly) wives attend the Al-Anon meetings. The emphasis is on sharing ideas and experiences to get a better understanding of alcohol problems and to gain strength from mutual support. Al-Ateen groups are sponsored by adult Al-Anon members.

There are over 1,000 Al-Anon groups in the British Isles, and more than 30,000 worldwide. Contact them at 61 Great Dover Street, London SE1 4YF. Tel. 0171-403 0888.

11

WORKERS IN THE ALCOHOL FIELD:
Three Alternatives in Treatment

A day centre

Women's groups for drinkers are still the exception, but centres like ACCEPT (Alcohol Community Centres for Education, Prevention and Treatment) have run women's groups as part of their treatment programme (in 1994 only one of its branches survives) .

ACCEPT in Fulham has been one of England's largest alcohol clinics and it was unusual for its high proportion (nearly half) of women clients. The clinic's former director, Charles Vetter, thinks this is a reflection of sexism in the conventional treatment field:

> Male treatment systems, male literature (i.e. a booklet entitled *So Your Husband Has a Drinking Problem* and no booklet *So Your Wife Has a Drinking Problem*), male doctors and consultants, males in the past having greatly outnumbered females in treatment, all these factors have led to male chauvinism in the alcohol field and the theory that women are more difficult to treat than men.
>
> Perhaps women are more difficult to treat than men, but they deserve an equal opportunity in treatment. We use a high proportion of women as counsellors – which in turn attracts women as clients.

Most of these clients had been triggered into drinking heavily by events in their lives which left them with feelings of loss – such as a death in the family, a broken marriage or romance, or children leaving home:

> We have one client who was a 'social drinker' for fifty years. Then her sister died, she suffered a lot of stress, and within three months she was drinking two to four bottles of sherry a day.
>
> Most women begin drinking in the first place as a consequence of social pressure. Men often think that pressurizing a woman to drink is a good way to lower her sexual defences. I used to be a world champion male chauvinist pig[1] and when I wanted to get a woman to bed I would buy her a lot of drink in the hope that it would make her more amenable.

For women the consequences of such tactics can lead to enormous guilt and shame – and unwanted pregnancy. One Birmingham birth-control clinic has found that of the women who asked for the morning-after pill, a high proportion reported drinking heavily.

Men tend to start drinking for different reasons from women: this is Charles's explanation:

> Men's drinking is part of the manhood ritual of growing up. Then it is a question of drink sneaking up on them. Men are more inclined to feel stress as the result of their jobs. For instance, a man who gets promoted may feel under a lot of pressure which he then tries to relieve with drink.
>
> Women are conditioned to look for different things in life from men, and are trained into being household slaves, mothers and cooks.
>
> Most women don't have any choice. They are trapped. Women are supposed to get their jollies through others which can lead to feelings of emptiness and depression.

And deferring to males is a very powerful syndrome. By not asserting themselves, women lose their self-esteem, they feel resentments and emotional discomforts. One way to relieve this is with alcohol.

Vetter is fond of referring to what he calls the Used Car Syndrome, in which a husband treats his drinking wife as if she was his car:

He expects daily, reliable service from her including her work as a household slave, as child minder, cook and sexual object.

When she 'breaks down' (i.e. starts drinking heavily) and neglects her chores, he will bring her in for 'repairs'. He will diligently resist any self-examination or counselling to develop insight into his role in creating marriage problems.

This is not at all unusual behaviour on the part of husbands. I had one man who brought his wife in and reeled off a list of complaints: she wasn't doing this, she wasn't doing that, the dinner wasn't ready, the house wasn't clean. He read me his Bill of Indictment and said, 'I'm leaving her here with you'.

After she'd been through treatment, she went home, and it was only a few weeks before she again 'broke down'. The husband rang me up and indignantly told me, 'You haven't done her a bit of good' - implying that his 'used car' is unreliable and that the 'garage' (the treatment agency) is guilty of poor workmanship.

In certain cases, after repeated breakdowns, and when the husband can afford it, he will trade in his 'used car', his wife, for a new model.

And leaving their spouse because of drinking is something husbands are far more likely to do than wives, largely because men tend to have more economic freedom than women:

Men can move to a new town, get a new job, find a new

partner more easily than women. And an older man can find a younger woman more easily than an older woman can find a new husband.

Women also tend to be more caring and loyal. They are trained from childhood to protect the family – and so often protect their drinking husband – which makes the situation worse.

In the ACCEPT relatives' group (for relatives to learn how best to help the drinker in their family), women have outnumbered men by ten to one.

A counsellor's experience: Jean Clack worked as a counsellor at ACCEPT from 1979. She found little difference, except in degree, between the underlying problems of women who had resorted to drink, and the problems of women in general.

Jean has never had a drink problem, but as she trained to become a counsellor she became aware of the other difficulties which hampered her as a woman – and which she now regularly encounters in her clients:

> At forty-one I went through a 'middle-age crisis'. I didn't know what I was doing with my life. I had been at home for so many years before I started work at ACCEPT that my self-esteem was very low. I did have a job in the City when I was younger, but by the time I was forty I had come to believe that I would never be able to work again. The ACCEPT programme of assertiveness-training and group therapy helped me to recognize that I still had an opportunity to do something which interested me.
>
> I find that the women who come to the clinic often have the same difficulties that I had myself – low self-esteem, oppressive conditioning and the man-woman thing.

Jean commonly saw women who were experiencing conflicts between their personal needs and the behaviour expected of them in the traditional roles of wife or mother or lover:

> 'I can't come in this evening as I've got to be home to get
> Johnny's tea' – that's the kind of thing they tell me. Then I
> discover that Johnny is sixteen. 'But I've always done it,'
> they say. I tell them it might do Johnny some good to take
> care of his mother for a change.

As women became more assertive in the course of the ACCEPT
programme, their husbands were inclined to feel threatened:

> The husbands feel fear when they find they've got a new
> person on their hands. We encourage relatives of clients to
> attend the relatives' groups – and husbands tend to get
> angry during the sessions. Sometimes the relationship
> breaks down altogether, which, in some cases, is
> appropriate.

Other women clients had worries about domestic duties:

> Either they are having trouble keeping up with their
> housework, or they are so obsessed with doing housework
> that they have to face the terrible problem of – what next?
> –when it gets to eleven o'clock.

Jean believes that women can only tackle these problems when
we grasp hold of the idea that we have our own rights as individuals. Some women who went to the clinic said that they were
motivated to attend by other people. One of Jean's clients began
the programme saying she was doing it for her son. But after a
while she was saying, 'Sod it, I'm doing it for *me*.'

Jean is not anti-drinking per se. But she does believe that
women who have been drinking in order to release inhibitions
and express their emotions can learn to do this without risking
dependency on alcohol:

> You can learn to get these feelings going, express these
> pent-up emotions – like anger – without drink. If you release

them while drinking no one takes much notice anyway.

Jean's observations are borne out by these comments, written in note form after an art class by one of ACCEPT's woman clients:

> From the cradle to the grave society is concerned with jobs, incomes, mortgages, politics, etc. Individuals continue on a dull treadmill with little opportunity to discover that they can develop an inner life of their own. (Hence also maimed personalities.)
>
> It is often difficult to communicate and 'dig out' problems through words . . . many people cannot express emotions in words. Sometimes it must be easier for them to express their feelings with their hands – especially if they feel they are being left to do their own thing.
>
> Whatever is stored inside us rots. Whatever comes out can be put to advantage – as can be seen from a very beautiful and sensitive drawing made by a man whose hand was shaking so much that he could not hold a coffee cup.

(These notes, written to Charles Vetter, end with an apologetic and self-deprecatory postscript: 'Charles, these are only notes. I am not too sure what you wanted. I do not wish to teach my grandmother how to suck eggs.')

And what happened to women's lives *after* going through the ACCEPT programme? Jean reflects on her own experience:

> Many women make big changes. Some go back to work after being at home for years. Look at me for instance. I changed roles completely and now I'm doing a full-time job. My family felt very threatened at first. One of my children (who took a year and a half to tell me) eventually said - I'm glad now that you went back to work. You're not so moody and I don't feel I've done everything wrong all the time.

A residential house

Whereas day centres like ACCEPT have been appropriate to the needs of problem drinkers who still have a home to go to, others who have lost their homes need a different kind of support.

Fiona Richmond is a social worker for London's Alcoholics Recovery Project (ARP). She runs a mixed residential house.[2]

She has worked with many women, each of whom has had problems particular to their individual circumstances. But she has found that there are broad patterns of drinking amongst women, which are related to our social position and the pressures on women. In simplified terms she characterizes her clients' problems like this:

> Some women who go the traditional way of marriage and children find that it doesn't make them happy. They feel unsatisfied, unfulfilled or feel the demands upon them are too great.
>
> One of my clients who married very young always felt she had to live up to the high expectations of her husband. He had rigid ideas about how his children should be brought up, how the house should be perfectly kept, etc.
>
> He was a farmer and she shared much of his work, doing the accounts and entertaining farm reps when they came to visit. Yet this woman never felt she was good enough. And so she drank to give her the confidence to act the role which was expected of her.

Another of Fiona's clients had a life that was miserable by any standards. After early marriage and early divorce she worked very hard in Scotland to bring up her child alone:

> For thirty years her life was a drudge. She drank for energy to get on with things at the end of the day, and to seek oblivion from her life. She felt at the same time resentful that she was being forced into living up to being a 'good

mother' – and a 'failure', as she felt that this wasn't really the case. 'I *should* have been able to do it,' is how she puts it now. She is a victim of imposed pressure from the expectations of society.

Then there is the woman who doesn't get married and who doesn't have children. Her feeling is 'there's something wrong with me'. She might be very successful in her work (one of Fiona's clients who felt this was qualified and employed as a nurse) but underneath she feels worthless. The conflict between what is expected of her and what she *feels* is such that she 'needs' alcohol to blot it out.

And in recent years Fiona has noticed a considerable increase in the number of young women needing treatment who have been drinking since their early teens. Sometimes these women are suffering from unmet emotional needs.

One of Fiona's clients started life with rejection by her own mother, went on to a psychiatric locked institution at the age of eight, and grew up without love, without security and without skills. By the age of twenty she had made numerous suicide attempts, and had had a child which was subsequently taken from her. 'It is hard to know how to help her,' says Fiona. 'She drinks to escape the reality of what her life is like, and for comfort.'

As severe as the problems of her clients are, Fiona believes their experiences are relevant to other women drinkers. Their problems are not unique to a separate breed of persons called 'alcoholics'. She sees them as existing at the extreme end of a common line of experience:

The difference between 'alcoholics' and other drinkers is one of the level of drinking and the degree of problems which follow. The women I work with talk about 'how it was five years ago and how it could be again'. Most of them believe that if circumstances had been different, things would have been okay.

Fiona leads the group meetings in which the women are encouraged to talk about their feelings and to learn to communicate again without alcohol. In these meetings, sexuality emerges as a big issue: These women are victims of strong stereotypes about what women should be. Feminine identity is hard enough to establish for any woman, but the 'unfeminine' problem of being a drinker aggravates the situation. They feel it is bad enough to be a drinker – but extra-bad because you are a woman.

> Women receive many 'messages' from society about what they 'are' or what they 'should be' as women. My clients talk about the extremes of being a woman: either you are meant to be perfect, giving, loving and all-caring. Or, at the other extreme, you are a whore and a slut. They talk about wanting to be the first kind of ideal woman – but feeling like the second. They say – 'I'm only a slut.'

In Fiona's experience there are essential differences between women and men when it comes to drinking – and some important parallels:

> Men will put their drinking down to environmental causes. They will say – it was my job. Or – we all did it. Or sometimes it is emotional, for instance – when my wife left me.
>
> But women usually put their drinking down to emotional needs. They are inclined to suffer from a sense of inadequacy, depression and lack of confidence.
>
> Another important difference is that men drink in public but women do it privately. My women clients talk about drinking behind locked doors, closing the windows and curtains – just me and the bottle.

Where men and women are alike is that both sexes will drink when what is expected of them doesn't fit with what they are:

The vulnerable man who feels he should be macho may drink to ease the strain. It is a political issue: the ways in which society defines us does damage to both sexes.

A women's group

Ann Hall is a social worker who, after years of experience in the alcohol field,[3] saw that the needs of her women clients were not being met by any of the existing facilities. Drawing on the lessons of the women's movement about the value of supportive, consciousness-raising, women-only groups, she decided (together with her colleague Jo Cleary), to set up such a group for women problem drinkers.

The women in this group, aged from twenty-five to thirty-five, had all experienced severe problems as a consequence of their drinking. Some had been in trouble with the law, and one woman had lost her eyesight as the result of a fight. Yet most had paid jobs – some were secretaries, some were teachers – and were coping well with other aspects of their lives.

The specific reasons why people drink are as individual as the person, but as the women in this group discussed their common experiences, a pattern began to emerge which Ann describes:

We found that the preoccupations of the drinkers in our group were very much of the kind that feminists identify as women's problems – difficulties with relationships, lack of assertiveness, the inability to express anger, and the loneliness and depression which stem from being stuck at home.

From the beginning we decided that the group was there not to talk about drinking as such, but to look at what was behind the drinking and to discover the million other underlying problems. What we found was the desire to forget, to blot out, to not cope, to do things without being responsible and without remembering. And the desire to be 'me' – without being hurt.

Anxiety was also a major factor. The women would describe themselves as feeling generally strung up. Whether this was a cause or a result of drinking, I don't know. We had many unresolved arguments about it. For most of them their anxiety was a panic about the effort of living, the feeling that I don't fit into all this, that I'm not very good at anything, that I'm inferior. That I don't like recognizing my needs for other people. That I don't like being vulnerable.

Acceptance of self was a fundamental problem for the women in the group:

Many of them were trying to come to terms with who they were and what they wanted. Many of the women also found it difficult to recognize and express their sexual needs. The permission thing came out very strongly – the feeling that I *shouldn't* be like this.

They felt – other people don't like me, I've got nothing to offer, I'm worthless. They felt – I've not done what I'm supposed to do, i.e. get a man, have kids.

But most of the women didn't really want this anyway. What they *did* want was to be valued, loved, respected, to be interesting, to be able to cope on their own. What they needed was confidence, assertiveness, belief in self, a sense of their own value.

Jo and I decided early on that we were not going to make any kind of condemnation of drinking behaviour in the group. And then on one occasion most of the group got together socially and went on a massive bender. They all got very drunk, continued drinking at a night club, got themselves into trouble and were nearly arrested.

At the next group meeting after this drinking bout we made no comment about the incident. The women reacted with anger. They wanted us to collude in their guilt by telling them they were wrong for doing it. They wanted us to take the responsibility. We didn't, and it was a turning point in the group. The women started to take responsibility for themselves.

Many of the techniques of psychotherapy were used to explore the group's legacy of unexplored feelings. Ann was struck by the women's inability to express anger:

Most of them had had pretty bad experiences, with their parents for instance, but had never expressed any anger.

One woman in the group had a schizophrenic father and brother, and she was carrying the whole weight of that family at the age of twenty-two. She would drink and drink and drink to escape. She was caring for all the others at the expense of herself. We wanted her to get angry and to start saying, I'm important, but we never quite achieved it.

On one occasion another woman in the group *did* get angry for the first time and she started shouting that she hated her family. All the tensions in the group exploded at once.

We realized after that that a lot of the women had never been able to say that they needed things. They had always felt guilty about wanting things, about making demands, about saying that their feelings mattered. Some of them were saying, I'm important, for the first time ever.

Ann believes that the group itself not only provided its own tools for discovering the problems behind drinking, but that it helped the women to support each other in very positive and practical ways. Eventually the women came to see that it was possible for them to make important changes in their lives – a vital realization for women whose choices are restricted on all sides:

Housing, family, restraints and money were problems for most of them. These social and political issues are inseparable from women's drinking.

12

THE PROBLEM SHARED

When women are harmed by others' drinking

Women suffer the consequences of alcohol abuse not only as drinkers, but as partners, relatives, wives, mothers, daughters or friends of other people who have drinking problems.

This is a notoriously complex (but certainly not impossible) situation to unravel. Often the woman who is close to a problem drinker has become as 'sick' as the drinker: she has survived years of anxiety, stress, fear, mixed emotions, manipulation and anger. She may well have suffered severe abuse and attacks on her self-esteem. She might have been subject to physical violence too. She could be drinking too much herself and be suffering from depression.

Often the woman who suffers from a partner's drink problem had a parent or grandparent with the same problems. A study started in 1960 of 229 children with 'alcoholic' fathers showed that nearly one-third suffered serious emotional disturbance.[1]

A growing realization of how parents' drinking can affect the future lives of their children has led to the Adult Children of Alcoholics movement which has swept the United States. And in Britain as well as the US, many self-help groups have sprung up to tackle the problems of 'women who love too much' – after Robin Norwood's hugely popular book of the same name. Norwood clearly hit a vital nerve when she described the compulsion of 'co-alcoholic' women (often with an 'alcoholic' parent) to try to 'rescue' and 'redeem' men with drink problems.

In many ways the traditional expectation that women should be 'caring' keeps the whole merry-go-round turning. For people who are abusing alcohol can't carry on for ever without someone to take care of them, to cover up and make excuses, to protect them and even supply them with booze. Indeed, people with alcohol problems are often attracted to those who they know will make things easier for them.

It is hard for women – who have been brought up to put other people's (especially men's) needs ahead of their own – to refuse 'help' to someone in a bad state, even when that 'help' is really helping the drinker to carry on drinking. For a woman to come to terms with the drinker in her life may mean (apparently) rejecting the nurturing role she has been expected to play since childhood. She will have to learn to stop putting the drinker's needs ahead of her own. She will have to learn to be 'selfish' – which women are certainly not supposed to be.

The low self-esteem and lack of confidence that our society instils in many women also sets us up to be more accepting of personal abuse and misery, while the need to please men and the fathomless guilt of many women are fertile ground for the manipulations of the heavy drinker.

Eric Appleby of Alcohol Concern says that he gets letters from wives of problem drinkers seeking reassurance that it is okay for them to be fed up with a husband's behaviour – even in a situation when the drinking husband is using violence against the wife. Women who live with a problem drinker often say they have given up expecting pleasure or happiness from life. They are trapped in a feeling of utter helplessness, trying their utmost not to let things get any worse.

There is another social factor that has long made it nigh impossible for women to break the vicious circle that binds them to heavy-drinking male partners, and that is money. How can you leave a husband if you can't afford to support yourself and your children without him? Only when women can earn a decent living and can afford a home of their own do they have any real choice in the matter. Yet many of today's single parents are forced to live in poverty. As in so many other aspects of our relationship with alcohol, when it comes to dealing with the problem drinkers in our lives, women's position in society is at the heart of the matter.

Coming to terms

The intricate web that binds a woman to a problem drinker is difficult to unravel, but it can be done. In the UK – and across the world – the most widespread organization to provide support for those involved with 'alcoholics' is Al-Anon.

In (usually) weekly meetings people of all ages and backgrounds gather to talk about how they got involved with a problem drinker, how the drinking has affected them and what they can do about it. Time and again the same issues crop up. Often a woman will have tried for years to protect the drinker from the consequences of drinking. She will have lied for him, supported him and made endless excuses for him.

Janet was in her late thirties when she began going to Al-Anon meetings. She was looking for a way to come to terms with her husband's drinking – and the role she had played in it:

> I've always had heavy drinkers in my life: first my father, then my boyfriends and then my husband Hugh. Of course I drank a lot too. I met Hugh in a pub, and when we started going out together it was always to a pub. Why should I object? I liked drinking too and I thought it was all quite normal.
>
> The problems began to develop slowly over a period of about ten years. Hugh began to get drunk much more easily than before, and he would get depressed and touchy – especially the next morning. He was never violent, but he

was verbally aggressive and very boring when he was
drunk. I could never get him out of the pub before closing
time, and he was forever coming home too drunk to eat
anything.

He was upsetting a lot of our friends too, and I was trying
to defend him in public while having terrible rows with him
in private. He did give up drinking several times – and in
one of those periods we had a child – but he always went
back to it, and each time he started again, he was worse
than before.

As Hugh's problems got worse, Janet found he depended more
and more upon her. Meanwhile she was becoming increasingly
distressed – and increasingly isolated – as their friends got fed up
with Hugh's behaviour. A woman with young children can be
lonely enough in our society, cut off as she is from much of adult
life and working within her own four walls for much of the day.
But when she knows her old friends and family are baffled and
hurt by her husband's behaviour the isolation becomes all the
more extreme. It is a lonely business too when the partner you
have always shared with and talked to 'disappears' into the
oblivion of alcohol:

He started to miss a lot of days at work. He would get me to
ring his boss and say he had a bad back and couldn't come
in. He would lie in bed for most of the morning, and then go
down to the pub again. Not surprisingly, he lost his job in
the end, but that was a terrible blow to him and he seemed
to get more and more depressed and permanently drunk.

I had to work part time to support us after his job went,
but we began to get more and more into debt. His drinking
cost a lot, and then he got into trouble a couple of times,
crashing the car when he was drunk.

Eventually, Janet decided they would have to move to another
town. Houses were cheaper so they could pay off some debts,

and she hoped that it might be a new start for Hugh. She didn't know it at the time, but as her friends in Al-Anon later told her, this is one of the classic steps in the downward curve of drink problems and it is called 'doing a geographical'. She soon found that it didn't solve anything. The family had taken their problems with them to their new home:

> Hugh's drinking didn't stop after we moved. In fact the only people he met in the new place were people at the local pub. By now his health was really going downhill. He could hardly eat – just lived off the booze – and we were stuck in an awful trap of drinking and arguing and saying sorry and starting all over again. It was as if the man I loved was being buried alive and I couldn't get him free. I felt angry and afraid and totally useless.

Only later, when Janet went to Al-Anon, did she hear other women in her situation talking about how to 'detach with love' from the drinker, so that he (or she) is forced to take responsibility for his (or her) own life. This strategy of 'tough love' is often discussed at Al-Anon groups, but in her own way, Janet had already begun the process:

> That year I made the decision to stop propping him up. We had two children by now and I was afraid for their safety and their future. I mentally cut myself off from him and stopped communicating. I started doing everything without him. I locked the bedroom door against him and in my mind I was looking for another relationship to help me break out of the one I was in.

Janet had also been trying off and on for years to get some medical help for Hugh, but she was fortunate that their new home was in an area with a good hospital alcohol treatment unit (like many ATUs, this one was closed down by 1990):

> I went to our GP and told him I was desperate. The GP made

an appointment with a psychiatrist, and – luckily that day Hugh had a terrible hangover. I took him to the appointment and sat there with him. The psychiatrist said I should take him to the psychiatric hospital which had an alcohol treatment unit.

I took him to the hospital and just left him there. He went through awful withdrawal symptoms, vomiting, disoriented and suicidally depressed. But after a few weeks he started to get better. It was like a miracle. He was quite a different person: sensitive and vulnerable. Like the Hugh I had originally fallen in love with. When he came home, first on weekends, then for longer stays, it was like a second honeymoon for us. Just to sit and talk was heaven. And he began a whole new relationship with the children. I never thought I would be that happy again.

But there were still many problems for Janet to sort out after Hugh eventually came home. Apart from the practical difficulties of rebuilding a new life, repaying debts and mending old friendships, she had yet to come to terms with her role in Hugh's drinking. He had been in hospital for months, receiving expert counselling and group therapy. Yet she had been forced to carry on at home, still under stress, earning a living and caring for the children. She went to Al-Anon for some years after Hugh had stopped drinking to try to work out for herself what had happened – and to prepare herself in case he started drinking again.

Seeking help

Al-Anon does have much to offer: chiefly the warm support and invaluable experience of other people who have been through the same agony. (Al-Ateen is the equivalent organization for young people, often concerned with a parent's drinking.)

The emphasis at Al-Anon is on letting go of your 'obsession' with the drinker's problems and trying to rebuild your own life as best you can. Then the drinker may well react to your changed behaviour – and the polite refusal to continue in the supporting role – by taking responsibility for his or her own actions.

But these groups do not suit everyone. Alcohol Concern's information officer Caroline Ray says that she gets calls from people who are disillusioned with Al-Anon because they were made to feel they could do nothing for the drinker until he or she 'reached rock bottom' and decided to change.

Yet the alternatives are few and far between. Some alcohol agencies have relatives' groups, but these vary depending on where you live. Contact Alcohol Concern to find out about services in your area, or look in the phone book.

The private alcohol treatment agencies also have relatives' groups, and in some cases their fees can be adjusted to your income. Or if you have a partner with drinking problems, try your local 'Relate' (the Scottish Marriage Guidance Council in Scotland). A sensitive Relate counsellor should be able to help you uncover a new perspective on your own family background and relationships so that you can begin to see where and why problems have cropped up – and if there are any patterns that you should look out for.

If you (and/or your children) are being abused or are at risk of abuse, Women's Aid will try to help you. Contact them at 52 Featherstone Street, London EC 1, or Scottish Women's Aid at 11 St Colme Street, Edinburgh EH3 6AG.

Or if you would just like the chance to think about and work through the problem on your own first, a good self-help manual is *Living With a Drinker: How To Change Things*, by Mary Wilson of the Scottish Council on Alcohol (Thorsons, 1989).

Another book which has helped many women to a clearer understanding of their relationship to problem drinkers (although it is not specifically about this subject) is *Women Who Love Too Much*, by Robin Norwood (Arrow, 1987). It has also been the spur to many a self-help group for women. In her book, Ms Norwood compared the progression of 'loving too much' and recovery with that of alcohol addiction and recovery illustrated in diagram 6, which is reproduced here by kind permission of Dr M. M. Glatt and the *British Journal of Addiction*.

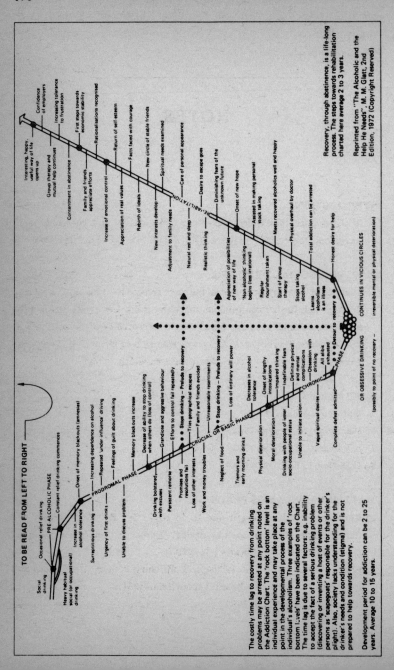

NOTES

INTRODUCTION
1. R. G. Ferrence, 'Sex Differences in the Prevalence of Problem Drinking' in *Alcohol and Drug Problems in Women*, O. J. Kalant (ed.), Plenum Press, 1980.

CHAPTER 2: SOCIAL DRINKING
1. That 'social' drinkers give many of the same reasons for drinking as 'problem' drinkers do is further confirmation that there is no clear divide between the two types of drinking pattern. See chapter 6 for discussion of terms.
2. Bill Saunders, 'Psychological Aspects of Women and Alcohol', in *Women and Alcohol*, Camberwell Council on Alcoholism, Tavistock, 1980.
3. *Daily Mail*, 13 April 1992.
4. Bill Saunders, op. cit.
5. *Daily Star*, 30 March 1994.
6. *Daily Telegraph*, 11 June 1990.
7. *Independent*, 27 October 1993.
8. *Daily Mail*, 15 February 1994.

CHAPTER 3 A WOMAN'S PLACE
1. Brovermann, I. K., Brovermann, D. M. *et al.*, 'Sex Role Stereotyping and Clinical Judgements of Mental Health', *Journal of Consulting and Clinical Psychology*, vol. 34, Part 1, pages 1-7, 1970.
2. Bridget Hutter and Gillian Williams, 'Controlling Women: The Normal and the Deviant' in *Controlling Women*, Croom Helm, 1981.
3. 'Herself Appraised', ASA 1992.

4. Shirley Otto, 'Women, Alcohol and Social Control', in *Controlling Women, op. cit.*

5. Nancy Mitford, *Zelda Fitzgerald*, Bodley Head, 1970.

6. Junius Adams and Michael Leitch, *Alcohol*, Omnibus Press, 1978.

7. Shirley Otto, *op. cit.*

8. Report from First DAWN Symposium, 28 November 1980. From London Council on Alcoholism, 146 Queen Victoria Street, London EC4.

9. Shirley Otto, *op. cit.*

10. *Daily Star*, 19 August 1993.

11. Hutter and Williams, *op. cit.*

CHAPTER 4: THE POLITICS OF ALCOHOL

1. 'Alcohol Policies in the UK', Report by the Central Policy Review Staff, May 1979. Published by Sociologiska Instituitonem, Stockholm Universitet, S106 91, Stockholm, Sweden, April 1982.

2. *About Women and Alcohol*, Scriptographic Publications Ltd, 1982.

3. FARE Newsletter Aug/Sept 1982. Women and Alcohol, Statistics.

4. OPCS General Household Survey, 1992.

5. *The Times*, 18 July 1991.

6. Admissions to mental illness hospitals by diagnosis, sex and year of admission 1979-86.

7. 'Alcoholics Anonymous, Survey of Alcoholics Anonymous in Great Britain', Report from General Service Board of AA, Great Britain Ltd, 1981. Available from Alcoholics Anonymous, P.O. Box 1, Stonebow House, Stonebow, York YO1 2NJ.

8. Brewers' Society Statistical Handbook 1986 (1987).

9. *Ibid.*

10. *Ibid.*

11. *Guardian*, 1 May 1990.

12. National Institute on Alcohol Abuse and Alcoholism, *Women and Alcohol*, May 1980. National Clearinghouse for Alcohol Information, P.O. Box 2345, Rockville, Maryland 20852, USA.

13. *Ibid.*

14. R. E. Kendell, 'Alcoholism: A Medical or a Political Problem?', *British Medical Journal*, 10 February 1979.

15. *Daily Mail*, 4 June 1990.

16. London De-Tox Study, 1989.

17. Stan Shaw, 'The Causes of Increasing Drinking Problems Amongst Women' in *Women and Alcohol*, Camberwell Council on Alcoholism, Tavistock, 1980.

18. *Ibid*.

19. Office of Health Economics, 'Alcohol, Reducing the Harm', April 1981. Available from 12 Whitehall, London SW1.

20. *Ibid*.

21. S. Ledermann, *Alcool, Alcoolisme, Alcoolisation*, Paris, Presses Universitaires de France, 1956.

22. R. E. Kendell, *op. cit*.

23. *Ibid*.

24. *The Times*, September 1993.

25. *Alcohol Health and Research World* vol. 17, no. 2, pages 137-143.

26. House of Commons Expenditure Committee (1977), 'Report on Preventive Medicine', vols 1-3, HMSO, London. See also Royal College of Psychiatrists (1979), 'Alcohol and Alcoholism', Tavistock; Advisory Committee on Alcoholism (1978), 'Report on Prevention', DHSS and Welsh Office: London; World Health Organization (1980), 'Problems Related to Alcohol Consumption', Technical Report Series No. 650, WHO, Geneva.

27. 'Alcohol Policies in the UK', *op. cit*.

28. 'Cirrhosis as a Growth Investment Opportunity?' Editorial in *British Journal of Addiction*, 77, 1982.

29. DHSS, 'Drinking Sensibly', HMSO, London, 1981.

30. *Drink Pocket Book*, NTC Publications, 1994.

31. *Labour Research*, 1980, no. 69, page 173.

32. *Labour Research, op. cit.*, pages 170-72.

33. Richard Smith, 'Alcohol and Alcoholism: The Politics of Alcohol', British Medical Journal, 8 May 1982.

34. Mike Daube, 'Disorderly House' in *Times Health Supplement*, 25 December 1981.

35. *Ibid*.

36. *Ibid*.

37. *Ibid*.

38. Richard Smith, *op. cit*.

39. Mike Daube, *op. cit*.

40. DHSS and NCVO, 'National Voluntary Organizations and Alcohol Misuse', September 1982.
41. *Daily Express,* December 1991.
42. 'Alcohol Policies in the UK', *op. cit.*
43. 'Cirrhosis as a Growth Investment Opportunity?', *op. cit.*
44. *Ibid.*

CHAPTER 5: BAD NEWS FOR WOMEN DRINKERS

1. Office of Health Economics, 'Alcohol: Reducing the Harm', April 1981.
2. Avon Council on Alcoholism, 'Women and Alcohol: A Survey of Gateways to Treatment for Women in Avon, 1982', Avon Council on Alcoholism.
3. Dr H. D. Chalke, 'Man's Alcoholic Equal?', *British Journal on Alcohol and Alcoholism,* vol 16.2, 1981.
4. Camberwell Council on Alcoholism, *Women and Alcohol,* Tavistock, 1980.
5. Royal College of Physicians, *A Great and Growing Evil – The Medical Consequences of Alcohol Abuse,* Tavistock, 1987.
6. Avon Council on Alcoholism, *op. cit.*
7. Stuart Kuttner and Neil Blincow, 'Postal Parson's £100,000 Mission', in *Evening Standard,* 26 April 1977.
8. Maxine Feifer, 'Don't Start Your Baby on the Drink', *Forum,* vol. 12, no. 2.

CHAPTER 6: ABOUT ALCOHOL

1. Chafetz and Demone, 'Alcoholism and Society', OUP, New York, 1962.
2. National Council on Alcoholism, 'What Everyone Should Know about Alcohol', Scriptographic Publications, 1981.
3. Office of Health Economics, 'Alcohol: Reducing the Harm', April 1981.
4. J. Adams and M. Leitch, *Alcohol,* Omnibus Press, 1978.
5. National Council on Alcoholism, *op. cit.*
6. *Ibid.*
7. Office of Health Economics, *op. cit.*
8. Health Education Council, 'Facts About Alcohol', HEC, Hamilton House, Mabledon Place, London WC1H 9TX.
9. J. Adams and M. Leitch, *op. cit.*
10. *Ibid.*
11. *Ibid.*

CHAPTER 7: ALCOHOL IN YOUR BODY

1. *PMT, The Unrecognized Illness*, Judy Lever with the help of Dr M. Brush and B. Haynes, Melbourne House, London, 1979.
2. *Ibid.*
3. *Nature*, July 1994.
4. Royal College of General Practitioners, 'Women and Alcohol', HMSO, 1992.
5. Office of Health Economics, 'Alcohol: Reducing the Harm', April 1981.
6. *British Medical Bulletin*, 'Alcohol and Disease', 1982, vol. 38, Churchill Livingstone.
7. J. B. Saunders, 'Alcohol: An Important Cause of Hypertension', *British Medical Journal*, vol. 294, pages 1045-6, 1987.

CHAPTER 8: ALCOHOL AND PREGNANCY

1. Royal College of General Practitioners, *op. cit.*
2. National Council of Women, 'Alcohol and the Unborn Child: The Foetal Alcohol Syndrome', March 1980, National Council of Women, 36 Danbury Street, London N1.
3. *Ibid.*
4. An Streissguth, Sharon Landesmann-Dwyer, Joan C. Martin, David Smith, 'Teratogenic Effects of Alcohol in Humans and Laboratory Animals', *Science*, vol. 209, 18 July 1980.
5. P. Lemoine *et al., Ouest Med.* 25, 477, 1968. (English translation available from National Clearinghouse for Alcohol Information, Department STIAR, P.O. Box 2345, Rockville, Maryland 20852, USA.)
6. Kenneth Jones, David Smith *et al.*, 'Pattern of Malformation in Offspring of Chronic Alcoholic Mothers', *The Lancet*, 9 June 1973.
7. Ann Streissguth, *op. cit.*
8. National Council of Women, *op. cit.*
9. *Ibid.*
10. Ann Streissguth, *op. cit.*
11. Rosemary Kent, *Say When*, Sheldon Press, 1990.
12. Ann Streissguth, a lecture reported in *New Scientist*, 11 January 1979.
13. Pamela Dowdell, 'Alcohol and Pregnancy, A Review of the Literature 1968-80', *Nursing Times*, 21 October 1981.
14. Information and Feature Service, 'Women and Alcohol', August 1979,

National Clearinghouse for Alcohol Information.

15. *Sunday Times*, 15 November 1987.

16. Royal College of Psychiatrists, 'Addendum to Alcohol and Alcoholism', Tavistock, 1979.

17. David Smith, 'Alcohol Effects on the Fetus, Fetal Drug Syndrome', *American Academy of Pediatrics*, 1979.

18. Ruth Little, 'Drinking During Pregnancy: Implications for Public Health', *Alcohol Health and Research World*, Fall 1979.

19. Royal College of Physicians, *A Great and Growing Evil – The Medical Consequences of Alcohol Abuse*, Tavistock, 1987.

20. National Council of Women, *op. cit.*

21. Alison Macfarlane, 'Saving Money: Spending Lives', *Medicine in Society*, vol. 8, no. 1.

22. J. W. T. Dickerson, S. Baker, B. Barnes, 'Environmental Factors and Foetal Health – The Case for Pre-Conceptual Care', Foresight, Woodhurst, Hydestile, Godalming, Surrey GU8 4AY.

23. *Ibid.*

CHAPTER 9: HANGOVERS: 'THE WRATH OF GRAPES'

1. David Outerbridge, *The Hangover Handbook*, Pan, 1981.

2. *Ibid.*

3. Robert Linn, *You Can Drink and Stay Healthy*, Sphere, 1981.

4. David Outerbridge, *op. cit.*

CHAPTER 10: DO YOU HAVE A DRINKING PROBLEM?

1. A. Paton and J. B. Saunders, *British Medical Journal*, 7 November 1981.

2. Griffith Edwards, *The Treatment of Drinking Problems*, Grant and McIntyre, 1982.

3. Office of Health Economics, 'Alcohol: Reducing the Harm', 1981.

4. Max Glatt, *Alcoholism*, Hodder and Stoughton, 1982.

5. Office of Health Economics, *op. cit.*

6. *Ibid.*

7. DAWN and FARE Joint Conference Note, 1982.

8. *Ibid.*

9. Clare Wilson, 'The Family, Women and Alcohol', in *Women and Alcohol*,

Camberwell Council on Alcoholism, Tavistock, 1980.

CHAPTER 11: WORKERS IN THE ALCOHOL FIELD: THREE ALTERNATIVES IN TREATMENT

1. Vetter's 'non-sexist' self-image and pronouncements on male chauvinism need to be taken with a pinch of salt. His personality dominates the clinic, and in our interview he literally talked down to me (seated on a low chair) from his large desk, his back to the light. On one occasion when I arrived in the clinic with a hangover I felt uncomfortable with the 'assertiveness' of the staff, and my personal feeling was that if I had gone there in a low state for help with drinking problems, I would have felt quite unnerved. On the other hand, there is no doubt that this clinic is dynamic and forward-looking, and has helped many people.

2. Although Fiona is committed to the idea of a one-to-one gender ratio in the house, such is the shame and guilt felt by women alcoholics that they are reticent about coming forward and there are usually fewer women than men living in the house.

3. Ann started working in the alcohol field at the Alcoholics Recovery Project (ARP) in London in 1973. She subsequently ran a hostel for drinkers in Leicester between 1976 and 1979, and then worked for Camden Alcoholic Support Association (CASA) from 1979 to 1981, during which time she organized the women's group. She subsequently worked in the Single Homeless Project.

CHAPTER 12: THE PROBLEM SHARED

1. *Sunday Times*, 15 November 1987.

USEFUL ADDRESSES

ACCEPT,
200 Seagrave Road,
London SW6 1RQ.
Tel: 0171-381 3155

ACAPS (Alcohol Counselling
  and Prevention Service),
34 Electric Lane
London SW9.
Tel: 0171-737 3579
(Black women/women
  counsellors available.)

Alcohol Concern
Waterbridge House
32-36 Loman Street
London SE1 0EE.
Tel: 0171 928 7377

Alcoholics Anonymous
P.O. Box 1
Stonebow House
Stonebow
York YO1 2NJ.
Tel: 01904 644026

Al-Anon Family Groups UK
61 Great Dover Street
London SE1 4YF.
Tel: 0171-403 0888
(24-hour confidential phone line)

DAWN (Drugs and Alcohol,
  Women's Network)
30-31 Great Sutton Street
London EC1V 0DX.
Tel: 0171 253 6221

Drink Crisis Centre
124 Brook Drive
London SE11 4TQ.
Tel: 0171 820 9947

DRINKLINE
Weddel House
7th Floor
13-14 Smithfield
London EC1A 9DL.
Tel: 0171 332 0150
Helpline: 0171 332 0202
(6-11pm confidential phone-line,
365 days a year)

GLAAS (Greater London
   Association of Alcohol
   Services)
30-31 Great Sutton Street
London EC1V 0DX.
Tel: 0171 253 6221

Health Promotion Unit
Department of Health
Hawkins House
Pollbeg Street
Dublin 2
Ireland.
Tel: 01 6714711

Irish AA
109 South Circular Road
Leonard's Corner
Dublin 8
Ireland.
Tel: 01 4538998

Northern Ireland AA
152 Lisburn Road
Belfast BT9 6AJ.
Tel: 01232 681084

Northern Ireland Council on
   Alcohol
40 Elmwood Avenue
Belfast BT9 6AZ.
Tel: 01232 664434

Scottish Council on Alcohol
137-145 Sauchiehall Street
Glasgow G2 3EW.
Tel: 0141 333 9677

Southall Alcohol Advisory
   Service
24-hour answerphone:
   0181-574 5244
(For Asian people with alcohol
   problems. Support groups for
   women. Asian counsellors
   available.)

Women's Alcohol Centre
66 Drayton Park
London N5.
Tel: 0171-226 4581

INDEX

PREVENTING BREAST CANCER
The politics of an epidemic

Dr Cathy Read

Breast cancer is the most common cancer among women. It is predicted that across the world it will claim the lives of one million women annually by the turn of the century.

These deaths are preventable.

As Cathy Read argues in this powerful and provocative book, breast cancer is not the mysterious and unavoidable epidemic many would have us believe. Conventional medicine has failed to find a cure for breast cancer. This book addresses the root causes, which lie in our diet, environment and social structures. Breast cancer is not 'women's fault' – but it is not beyond our means to control it.

By laying bare the politics of an epidemic, *Preventing Breast Cancer* calls on everyone, women and health professionals alike, to stop the wringing of hands and unravel the real story behind breast cancer.

NATURAL HEALING FOR WOMEN
Caring for yourself with herbs, homoeopathy and essential oils

Susan Curtis and Romy Fraser

This vital reference book makes natural health a realistic part of busy stressful lives. Susan Curtis and Romy Fraser draw on many years' experience to explain the different needs of our energy and repair systems, and the natural healing options now available.

The Repertory of Ailments covers psychological as well as physical aiments – from anxiety to acne, colds to cancer – and explains conventional methods of treatment as well as the benefits of alternative approaches.

The Materia Medica is an A to Z of alternative remedies and treatments, including homoeopathy, herbalism, flower remedies and essential oils, with clear instructions on preparation and application.

Lifestyle contains practical and realistic guidelines for improving diet, exercise and sleep patterns, as well as relaxation techniques, a cleansing programme and a natural first aid kit.

These three sections combine to form a unique guide to healing mind, body and spirit.

OLDER MOTHERS
Conception, pregnancy and birth after 35

Julia Berryman, Karen Thorpe and Kate Windridge

Mothers over 35 are the fastest growing group of mothers in many countries, including Britain, the United States and Australia. But, apart from the odd sensational story, very little is known about them.

What kinds of women start or add to their families at this stage in life? And what are their experiences? Psychologists Julia Berryman, Karen Thorpe and Kate Windridge carried out unique international research on older mothers. Drawing on this as well as other studies they address a wide variety of issues, including:

- who has babies after 35, and why?
- what are the risks involved? And, how do women feel about them?
- is it harder to get pregnant?
- what is pregnancy like for older women? Does age make a difference?
- how are relationships and career affected?
- what is the actual birth like for older mothers and how do they cope with a new baby?
- and finally, what is it like to be the older mother of a child? And, what is it like for the child?

Using a careful mix of care histories and accessibly-presented research, *Older Mothers* is a rich and rounded picture of the joys and problems of motherhood after 35, which will be invaluable to any women considering giving birth later in life, as well as to all professionals involved in the field.

WOMEN AND HIV/AIDS
An international resource book

Marge Berer with Sunanda Ray

By the late 1980s AIDS had become one of the leading causes of death among women of reproductive age in many parts of the world. In the 1990s and beyond, women will be in the forefront of HIV/AIDS prevention and care. This book brings together a decade of knowledge and experience regarding the impact of HIV/AIDS on women's health, sexual relationships and reproductive rights – and what women are doing about it around the world.

'It is impossible to flick idly through this book. You'll constantly find yourself drawn into deeper reading. The sheer scope is astonishing, and unflaggingly presented in an accessible, thoughtful and fascinating way.'

JANET HADLEY, *Everywoman*

Preventing Breast Cancer	0 04 440909 5	£7.99 ☐
Older Mothers	0 04 440906 0	£8.99 ☐
Natural Healing for Women	0 04 440645 2	£8.99 ☐
Natural Healing for Gynaecology	0 86 358069 6	£5.99 ☐
Women and HIV/AIDS	0 04 440876 5	£14.99 ☐

All these books are available from your local bookseller or can be ordered direct from the publishers.

To order direct just tick the titles you want and fill in the form below:

Name: _____

Address: _____

_____

_____Postcode_____

Send to: Thorsons Mail Order, Dept 3, HarperCollins*Publishers*, Westerhill Road, Bishopbriggs, Glasgow G64 2QT.

Please enclose a cheque or postal order or your authority to debit your Visa/Access account –

Credit card no: _____

Expiry date: _____

Signature: _____

– to the value of the cover price plus:

UK & BFPO: Add £1.00 for the first book and 25p for each additional book ordered.

Overseas orders including Eire: Please add £2.95 service charge. Books will be sent by surface mail but quotes for animal despatches will be given on request.

24 HOUR TELEPHONE ORDERING SERVICE FOR ACCESS/VISA CARDHOLDERS – TEL: 041 772 2281.